STARTING WITH GOATS

The Guide to Keeping Goats for Smallholders and as Pets

Katie Thear

Broad Leys Media Ltd

Broad Leys Media Ltd
Fron Dirion
Clogwyn Melyn
CAERNARFON
LL54 6PT

www.blpbooks.co.uk
E-mail: books@broadleys.org

First edition published by Broad Leys Publishing Ltd: 2006
Second edition published by Broad Leys Media Ltd: 2014

A copy of the British Library Cataloguing in Publication
Data is available from the British Library

Book cover, interior and e-book design by Velin@Perseus-Design.com

ISBN: 978-0-906137-42-0

Outside front cover: British Saanen goat and kid. Anne Crossman

Back cover: Top: British Toggenburg goat and kid. Katie Thear
                Middle: Pygmy goat kid. Katie Thear
                Angora goat. Katie Thear

Please note that some of the photographs show goats that do not
have identifying ear tags as these photographs were taken before
regulatory changes making them a legal requirement.

Photographs and illustrations are by: Katie Thear, Peter Cox, Harry Fuller,
Stephen Whiteley, Margaret Merchant, Graham Turner and Anne Crossman.

For details of other publications please see page back page.

Contents

Preface

The first book that I wrote about goats was called *Goats and Goatkeeping* and was published by Merehurst in 1988. It was well received in Britain and internationally but has been out of print for a number of years.

Now that there is a resurgence of interest in goats, with new and potential goatkeepers appearing, it is appropriate to use it as the basis for a new book that is up-to-date in its coverage.

I hope that all those who are thinking of keeping goats will find it useful, and that those who have been kind enough to regard the original book as a favourite in the past will welcome its return in an updated form. Although now entitled *Starting with Goats*, it is still comprehensive enough to be useful to those who are more experienced goatkeepers.

I am grateful to the many goatkeepers who have helped by contributing in so many ways, including helpful suggestions, the loan of photographs and by welcoming me to their homes.

Katie Thear, Newport, 2006.

British Saanen milking goats in a communal pen. (Katie Thear)

Introduction

*Capricorn, the goat, a sign of the Zodiac between the Archer and the Waterman,
fought with Jupiter against the Titans.*
(Signs of the Zodiac).

Goats are intelligent and sensitive creatures, quick to respond to individual attention and affection. They do best in relatively small herds and are ideal for the small family farm or smallholding. Goats are sociable animals and should always have the company of their own kind.

There are many reasons for keeping goats. In my own case, the main reason was because my daughter was allergic to cow's milk. At the time, it was rare to find shops that sold goat's milk and it was obvious that we would have to produce it ourselves. Now, it is more easily available, but even so, it cannot compare in freshness with the home-produced variety.

Once we had our goats, we soon appreciated the other positive reasons for keeping them. They are real characters, and they became firm family pets. Goats soon learn their names and come when called. They are also much easier than cows to hand-milk, and their smaller size makes them generally easy to handle. All our children became proficient at helping to care for them.

The amount of milk the goats produced was just right for our family of five. It was enough for all our daily needs, as well as for the occasional production of yoghurt and cheese. Our past experience with keeping a house cow was that there was just too much milk. It could not be stored for long without having to be processed on a regular basis, and there are only so many hours in the day. Goat's milk has smaller butterfat particles that are dispersed throughout the volume of liquid so that it is naturally homogenised. Because of this it can be frozen and stored in the freezer until ready for use.

People have different requirements from their goats. A dairy breed such as the Saanen or Anglo-Nubian may be providing the family milk supply while a fibre breed such as the Angora may be a source of fibres for spinning. Pygmy goats are often kept as pets, while the large Boer goat provides meat. They may be kept as a commercial enterprise or for the household. Exhibiting good examples of their type is also popular, but whatever the scale or nature of the activity, the basic standards of good husbandry are the same: the need for proper housing, feeding, grazing and browsing, health care and a level of management that is appropriate to their innate needs.

Are Goats For You!

If you are interested in goats but have not yet come to a decision about whether or not to keep them, the following information may be useful.

For

They are sensitive, intelligent animals and readily respond to kind owners.

They are easy to tame and make good pets.

They need less land than larger animals such as cattle.

They are cheaper to buy and feed compared with larger stock.

They are browsers rather than grazers and eat a wide range of fibrous plants such as weeds and shrubs.

Their small size makes them easier to milk than larger dairy animals.

Their milk is more like human milk than cow's milk, making it suitable for those who are allergic to cow's milk.

The milk is 'naturally homogenised' so that it can be frozen until used.

The quantity of milk is right for the family, without producing a huge surplus.

Unlike cows, they do not need to give birth every year in order to produce milk.

There are breed societies and local goat clubs to provide help and support.

Against

They are herd not solitary animals and need another of their own kind.

All owners of goats must register them with DEFRA.

They must have identification tags.

Their movements on and off the site must be recorded.

All veterinary treatments need to be recorded.

Appropriate housing, exercising and milking areas are necessary.

Dairy goats need to be milked twice a day, while all goats need daily feeding and general care.

Food and hay/straw storage facilities are needed.

Goats will cause damage to trees and plants; gardens and orchards must be protected against them.

Regular foot trimming and health protection routines are required.

Regular 'mucking out' is necessary.

They are a permanent 'tie' and provision must be made in order to take holidays.

Although milk and dairy produce can be used at home, they cannot be sold without registration with the Environmental Health authority and meeting the requirements of the Dairying Regulations.

There are drawbacks, of course! Keeping animals carries responsibilities. They must be looked after and fed every day. Milk producers must be milked twice a day and regular mucking out of their housing is necessary. Arrangements need to be made for their care during holiday periods and if they fall ill, veterinary attention is essential. Although goats can be kept in relatively small areas, they are at their happiest when they have the freedom to browse larger areas of meadows and fields.

Goats are naturally inquisitive, so gardens and orchards will need to be protected against them. It is a popular misconception that goats will eat anything. In fact, they are highly selective eaters, choosing broad-leaved, fibrous plants such as weeds and branches from trees and shrubs as a source of dietary minerals. It is also a misconception that goats will act as lawnmowers, and keep down the grass. They are browsers rather than grazers. They eat grass but will not crop it short in the way that sheep will.

Where to start

Joining a local goat club is an excellent way of acquiring experience before buying. Goatkeepers in such societies are usually only too willing to help novices by showing them their livestock and offering a fund of good advice. The local library usually has details of local organisations or they may be had from the British Goat Society. Local societies are usually affiliated to the BGS.

You can also go on a course at one of various levels of management, from the basic introductory standard to full-blown commercial training. These are usually organised by agricultural colleges and other training organisations. At such courses it is possible to gain a great deal of experience in activities such as milking, giving worming preparations, foot trimming and so on. A potential buyer is then in a realistic position to take charge of goats.

Other essentials are to have all the buildings ready for occupation before the goats arrive, including all the necessary equipment.

Are there any regulations?

Anyone who keeps goats, regardless of the number, must register with their local DEFRA Animal Health Divisional Office (AHDO). They will issue the keeper with a County, Parish, Holding (CPH) Number for the site on which the goats are resident. After registration, the owner is issued with a Herd Registration Document (HRD) that allocates a unique herd mark to the owner.

Goats that have been born, or first identified, after 31st December 2009 must be identified within six months of birth when housed overnight; 9 months of birth if not housed overnight; and when they move off the holding of birth if this is sooner. A single identifier tag is required for any goats intended for slaughter before the age of 12 months. For all other goats two non-electronic identifiers are required, both of which should bare the same individual number. Electronic tags may be used by the keeper, but this is not a legal requirement.

When goats are moved from one site to another you must make a record in your own Holding Register as well as completing Movement Document AML1. There are variations in how you do this which are explained in the Keepers Handbook available from DEFRA. As of April 2014 goat keepers in England will be able to use the new Animal Reporting and Movements System (aRAMs) to electronically report their animals' movements.

A Record of Medicines should be kept, indicating what veterinary treatments have been given, the dates when commenced and finished and the identifying numbers of the treated animals. Any goat over 18 months that dies or is slaughtered (except for human consumption) must be reported to DEFRA. Those selling milk and dairy produce are required to meet the requirements of the Dairy Products (Hygiene) Regulations 1995.

Wild (Bezoar or Pasan) goat, ancestor of the domestic goat. *(Cyclopedia of Livestock. 1908)*

Early representation of goats in caves at Le Roc, Charente. *(Knowledge. Purnell. 1960)*

Coin of Aegospotami showing Demeter on the front and a goat on the reverse, commemorating the defeat of the Athenians by Lysander in BC 405 at Aegosflumen (the river of goats). *(Classical Dictionary. Smith. 1899)*

Goat depicted in a Roman mosaic floor at Merida in Spain. *(Katie Thear)*

Goats displaced during the Enclosures became feral and interbred with the remnants of the ancient wild goat populations in the mountainous areas of Britain. *(Common Goat. Thomas Bewick. 1790).*

During the 19th and 20th centuries Swiss and Nubian goats were imported to increase the productivity of British goats.

Although known earlier, most Angora goats came in the late 20th century. At the same time Cashmere goats began to create interest. They catered for the demand for quality fibres. *(Thomas Bewick. 1790)*

Boer goats were introduced for meat in the late 20th century. *(Boer Goat Society)*

Pygmy goats first introduced in the 1970s are now often kept as pets. *(Katie Thear)*

Castrated males are sometimes used as harness goats. *(Katie Thear)*

About the Goat

I'd rather have a naughty intelligent goat than a dumb good sheep.
(Schoolgirl during a talk on goats. 1980)

Goats have a long and chequered history. They have been associated with man since Palaeolithic times, with their images appearing in early cave rock carvings. It is likely that, along with the dog, they are the earliest animals to be domesticated. This is thought to have taken place in Neolithic times, around 10,000 years ago, when archaeological evidence indicates that they shared man's settlements. Recent DNA studies have shown that their main line of descent came from the Middle East, with later lines emanating from South East Asia and the Near East. The ancestor of the domestic goat is the wild Bezoar or Pasan goat.

It is not known when goats were first introduced to Britain but they could have been brought by any of the early settlers before these islands became separated from the rest of Europe. They were certainly here in Neolithic times because their bones have been found in early settlements such as Windmill Hill in Wiltshire. Further introductions may also have been brought by later immigrants.

There are still wild goats in the mountainous areas of Britain. They probably contain remnants of the Neolithic populations as well as those that were turned off the commons and became feral during the Enclosures and Clearances of the 17th to 19th centuries (see below). A population that is known to date back to 1380 is the one named after the Bagot family of Blithfield Hall in Staffordshire. It is also depicted in their coat of arms.

All the ancient civilisations, including the Greeks, Egyptians and Chinese kept goats. They were common in Biblical times and there are few societies which have not been involved with them to some degree. They held a place of honour in many ancient societies. Zeus, the king of the Gods was said to have been suckled by Amalthea, a she-goat, and as a result she and her kids were awarded their own constellation in the heavens. Goats have also appeared on ancient commemorative coins.

This popularity was not always apparent. As a species, they have been maligned and even persecuted. The Biblical allegory of pious sheep on the right hand side of God and capricious goats on the left, resulted in their being associated with hell, damnation and witchcraft. This is apparent in the iconography of the Judaic-Christian traditions. Goats were seen as fair game, even to be thrown from the top of church towers during religious festivals.

The Enclosure movement in the 17th to 19th centuries in England and Wales added to the general disparagement of goats, although they had played an important part in the lives of ordinary people. By annexing common land the aristocracy deprived large numbers of cottagers of their traditional grazing rights.

Although the long-term effect of the Enclosures was to increase overall agricultural production, the landless peasantry lost their main source of milk and dairy produce as goats and other livestock were turned off the commons. In Scotland the Highland clear¬ances had a similar effect; where the crofters were usurped, their goats were also displaced. Many of these animals reverted to the wild, either forming new herds of feral goats or adding to existing ones.

Sheep farmers and landowners were soon to wage a war of attrition against feral goats. The sheep farmers suspected goats of interbreeding with their flocks, while landowners looked on the goats' ability to encroach upon enclosed land as tantamount to a revolt of the lower orders. This attitude was passed on, with the goat often being described as the 'tinker's cow'. Until comparatively recently, little credence was given to the goat as a serious farm animal in Britain, although they have always held such a position in areas of mainland Europe such as Switzerland and France.

An important stage in the reversal of this attitude was the formation of the British Goat Society (BGS) in 1879. Its aims were to counteract the general prejudice against goats and to spread more accurate information about them. It encouraged people to keep them again and to set about improving and developing the dairying qualities of goats. The BGS is still active today and most local and breed clubs are affiliated to it.

The Toggenburg was introduced to Britain from Switzerland in 1882 with the aim of increasing milk production. Other breeds such as the Saanen, the Alpine and the Nubian followed and there was a considerable amount of cross-breeding with existing British goats in order to produce more productive dairy animals. Each of the breeds now has its own breed society affiliated to the BGS.

Pygmy goats began to arrive in these islands in the late 1970s, and are now popular as pets and as show animals. A Pygmy Goat Club was formed in 1982.

Castrated male goats are sometimes used as harness animals and a Harness Goat Society to promote them and look after their welfare was formed in 1987.

Boer goats for meat were introduced in the 1980s and their interests as a breed are now looked after by the British Boer Goat Society, an association that was formed in 1988.

Angora and Cashmere goats are renowned for their quality fibres. Although both are ancient breeds, and known about in Britain, they were not introduced in any numbers until the late 20th century. The Angora was imported from 1981 onwards, first from Australasia and subsequently from Canada. The British Angora Goat Society was formed in 1981

Cashmeres are any goats that produce substantial amounts of fine secondary or undercoat fibres. These keep the animal warm and are found in the greatest quantities in feral animals. Cashmere semen was imported into Britain from Iceland, Siberia, Tasmania and New Zealand and feral animals have also been used to develop the cashmere industry. The Scottish Cashmere Producers' Association was formed in 1985. The Macaulay Institute founded in 1987 is a research organisation involved in the development of Cashmere goats.

What to look for in a healthy goat

No horns (unless fibre goats)

No shaking of head

Ear tag identification

No swollen glands

Bright, alert eyes

Gradual slope of rump to tail

Long back, not too curved

Regular breathing; no nasal discharge

No excessive tail wagging

Well-shaped mouth; no dribbling

Clean vent area

Long, fine neck

Well-sprung, rounded rib cage

Hocks straight; wide apart

Clean glossy coat; no scurf or bare patches

Deep barrel body

Straight legs; no bandiness or swollen joints

Spherical silky udder with two well-shaped teats; no undue heat, lumps or clots in milk

Sound, well-trimmed feet and straight pasterns

Conformation of a dairy goat

The ideal dairy goat is wedge-shaped when viewed from the back, with rounded sides and a well-sprung rib cage

A named breed should be a good example of its type when compared with the standard for the particular breed.

Checking the udder

A good even udder

Misshapen udder

Extra teat; hard to milk

Fishtail teat: hard to milk

Jaws

Space

Horny pad on top jaw

Molar teeth

Incisor teeth on bottom jaw only

Incisor teeth on bottom jaw. In a kid they are small. By the time the goat is 4 years old they are fully grown and the same size

15

Classification

If we 'place' the domestic goat in its position relative to the rest of the animal kingdom, it is in the *Artiodactyla* or 'even-toed' order of mammals. This is a group that includes all the ruminants, plus the pigs and hippopotamuses. Within this order there are six families. Goats are in the *Bovidae* or 'hollow-horned' family. Other members are cattle, sheep, oxen, buffalo, bison, antelope, yaks and gnus. They are all creatures that have permanent horns, rather than those that are shed, such as those of the deer. (Some goats are born naturally polled, or hornless, but this is a genetic mutation from the norm).

The sub-family *Caprinae* includes goats and sheep, while the genus *Capra* is a category that includes nine species including ibexes, markhors and true goats:

Capra aegagrus	Wild Goat (Bezoar/Pasan)	*Terminology*	
Capra caucasia	West Caucasian Tur	Male goat	Male
Capra cylindricornis	East Caucasian Tur		Buck
Capra falcomeri	Markhor		Billy (archaic)
Capra ibex	Alpine Ibex	Female	Female
Capra nubiana	Nubian Ibex		Doe
Capra siberica	Siberian Ibex		Nanny (archaic)
Capra pyrenica	Spanish Ibex	Up to 1 year	Kid
Capra walie	Walie Ibex	Female 1-2	Goatling
		Male 1-2	Buckling
		In-milk	Milker
		In-milk goatling (without kidding)	Maiden milker

The Wild goat, *Capra aegagrus*, is the main ancestor of the domestic goat, *Capra aegagrus hircus*, although nobody knows what other Capra species may have contributed to its development. Some of the present Spanish breeds of goats, for example, have twisted horns that are reminiscent of some of the other species. No doubt, continuing DNA examinations will eventually explain the genetic connections between the various species.

Kingdom: *Animalia* (animals as distinct from plants)
Phylum: *Chordata* (having a spine)

16

Class: *Mammalia* (warm-blooded animals, born alive and suckled by mother)
Order: *Artiodactyla* (even-toed, includes ruminants, pigs and hippopotamuses)
Family: *Bovidae* (hollow-horned, includes cattle, sheep, buffalo, antelopes, yak, gnus)
Sub-family: *Caprinae* (sheep and goats)
Genus: *Capra* (nine species, as listed above)
Species: *Capra aegagrus* (wild goat)
Sub-species: *Capra aegagrus hircus* (domestic goat)

Note: There are slight discrepancies amongst the various classification systems. Some refer to the wild goat as *Capra hircus* and the domestic goat as *Capra hircus aegagrus*.

Characteristics of Goats

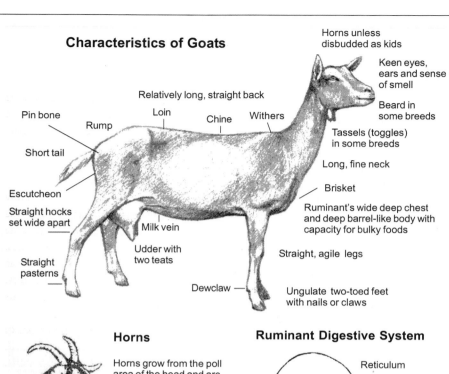

Horns unless disbudded as kids

Keen eyes, ears and sense of smell

Beard in some breeds

Tassels (toggles) in some breeds

Long, fine neck

Relatively long, straight back

Pin bone

Loin

Chine

Withers

Rump

Short tail

Escutcheon

Brisket

Straight hocks set wide apart

Ruminant's wide deep chest and deep barrel-like body with capacity for bulky foods

Milk vein

Udder with two teats

Straight, agile legs

Straight pasterns

Dewclaw

Ungulate two-toed feet with nails or claws

Horns

Horns grow from the poll area of the head and are used for protection. Kids are normally disbudded by a vet so that the horns do not grow for safety reasons.

Ruminant Digestive System

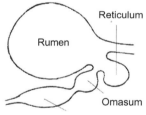

Reticulum

Rumen

Omasum

Abomasum

Structure of the Udder

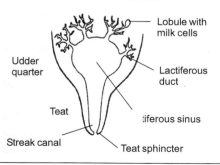

Lobule with milk cells

Udder quarter

Lactiferous duct

Teat

tiferous sinus

Streak canal

Teat sphincter

Structure of the foot

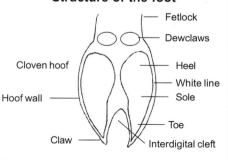

Fetlock

Dewclaws

Cloven hoof

Heel

White line

Hoof wall

Sole

Toe

Claw

Interdigital cleft

Characteristics

Whatever their origins, goats share the same basic characteristics. A knowledge of these allows for a better standard of management. It makes sense to provide conditions to suit the goats, as far as this is possible, rather than expect the goats to adapt to an unsuitable environment.

Ungulate

Goats are ungulates, in that they have cloven hooves with claws. They are essentially creatures of the heights, adapted to leaping and scrambling from one precipitous ledge to another. Their feet are beautifully adapted for this, with small hooves able to draw close together and balance on tiny areas. Years ago, as a child in Wales, I used to wonder at the stories which told of the wild mountain goats being able to stand on a space no bigger than an old penny. In particularly hard winters, they would descend and raid people's gardens before reverting to the mountainous heights. They still do so today!

Goats' feet have nails which grow continuously. In the wild, the effect of scrambling on rocks has the effect of keeping them worn down and short. In domestic situations, this is not so, and the feet must be trimmed on a regular basis. Although the provision of a scrambling area, particularly one which incorporates rocks, will help to keep foot trimming to a minimum, it does not do away with it. Further details of foot trimming are given on page 110.

It is a good idea to provide goats with a scrambling area for another reason, too. A group of logs placed at different heights, or a few paving stones allows them to follow their instinct for climbing. Kids and goatlings love them, and even older, more dignified matrons have been known to cast aside their dignity in favour of more capricious behaviour.

Ruminant

The goat is a ruminant, in other words, an animal that crops herbage quickly, partly chews and swallows it, then stores it in a special area of the stomach called a rumen. The food is then regurgitated and chewed at leisure, a process called 'chewing the cud'.

The stomach is divided into four distinct areas enabling it to consume large amounts of vegetation and digest it over a period of time. This system must have evolved to help ensure survival of the wild goat: like other ruminants, it could snatch herbage where available, then escape the possible attention of predatory carnivores to chew its food at leisure and in safety.

The natural behaviour of goats in the wild is to eat scrubby material at a certain height. This is thought to give them some protection from being infested with internal parasites, which are usually found in greater concentrations at ground level. You can observe part of this behavioural pattern when you feed hay to domestic goats; if any should fall from the hayrack on to the floor, they will not eat it.

The incisor or biting teeth are only found on the lower jaw. The upper jaw has a horny pad against which they bite. Behind is a space within the mouth cavity reaching to the molar or grinding teeth at the back. The relative size of the incisor teeth can be used to judge the age of a goat. In a kid they are all small and the same size. A goatling will have the two front ones larger than the others. By the time the goat is around two, there are four large teeth at the front. It is only when the goat is four years or more that the teeth are fully developed and all the same size.

Horns

Most goats have horns, although there are occasionally ones that are naturally polled when born. This is a genetic trait. It is not a good idea to breed from two such animals with the idea of developing a hornless strain, for the trait is also associated with infertility. A naturally polled animal should therefore only be crossed with a normal, horned one.

When kids are born, there are two small buds on the top or poll area of the head. These are the horn buds and it is normal for them to be cauterised by the vet when the kids are a few days old. This process of disbudding ensures that horns do not grow. Removal of the buds is considered to be veterinary surgery under the provisions of the Veterinary Surgeons Act 1966 and as such it must be carried out by a qualified veterinary surgeon.

As horns are natural features that are used for protection in the wild, why is it necessary to prevent their growth? Quite simply because they would present a hazard to their keepers and to each other, and domestic goats are not in the wild where they need to protect themselves against predators. Dairy goats are almost invariably disbudded, although fibre goats are usually left horned. Some Pygmy goats are also allowed to grow their horns, but as a general rule, it is much better and safer for all concerned, if all goats are disbudded as kids.

Gregarious

There are instances of a single goat living happily with a donkey, and in one case, of an inseparable relationship between a goat and a cat. As a general rule, however, it is better to avoid keeping a single animal. The goat is a herd animal, gregarious in its outlook. A single animal will transfer its attentions to its owner to the extent of wanting to be with him or her the whole time.

Need for shelter

Goats have a common dislike of rain, rapidly seeking shelter when the first drops arrive. This may have originated as a safety device during their evolution, preventing them from slipping on the wet rocks of the craggy heights. The other factor is that, unlike sheep, the coat does not have much oil in it to make it waterproof. It is important to bear this in mind, remembering to make shelter available for any animals, which may be out in a field and at the mercy of sudden showers.

Shelters should also be available when the sun is particularly strong. White goats have been known to suffer from sunburn, and in tropical areas they are more likely to develop skin cancers than coloured goats.

Some goatkeepers tether their goats outside but this is not recommended. Tethered goats cannot run to a shelter if the weather changes. They can also become tangled in the tether.

Capricious behaviour

Goats are capricious! Even their most ardent admirers have to admit it. They are intelligent and playful, but they are also devious and contrary. It has been said that goats have slit eyes to enable them to see round corners where the grass is greener. They are experts at opening gates and finding small gaps through which to squeeze. Washing on the line is an irresistible temptation, while fruit trees are there to be debarked and decimated.

The ability of goats to stand on their hind legs and perform intricate ballet steps in order to strip the top branches of their greenery is legendary. Effective confinement is essential if the relationship is to be a happy one, but the confined area needs to include plenty of interest for the goats. I have already mentioned a scrambling area. The other important necessity is roughage in the form of hay, cut branches, hedge prunings and general twiggy growth, placed in hay-racks so that they are clear of the ground. Hay is the single most important fibrous part

21

Goats are friendly and intelligent animals that relate well to their owners, but they should always be without horns in case of accidents. *(Katie Thear)*

of the diet and should always be available. Ensure that branches are not from poisonous plants and avoid areas that have been sprayed. (See page 55 for details of poisonous plants).

These, then, are the main characteristics of goats. A little forethought and effort made to provide them with conditions to their liking will help to produce contented, productive animals with a minimum of problems.

Acquiring Goats

She went to the tailor to buy him a coat.
When she came back he was riding a goat.
(Old Mother Hubbard. Traditional Nursery Rhyme)

Buying

Learning about goats and preparing their housing are the priorities (see the *Housing* chapter). Once the appropriate conditions are in place, it is time to think of getting the goats. However, there are still several other factors to be taken into consideration.

Decide on a breed

There are several breeds to choose from, and the choice will depend on whether the goats are for milk, fibre, exhibiting, breeding or for keeping as pets. Take into account the breed standards that apply to specific breeds, so that you are in a position to recognise good examples of their type. (See the *Breeds* chapter).

It may be that cross-bred goats are acceptable, and there are certainly good milkers to be found that are not pedigree animals.

Ask an experienced goatkeeper for help

Having an experienced goatkeeper for company is a good idea when buying a goat. A novice can make an expensive mistake through lack of experience and judgement. If a specific breed is required, the secretary of the breed society can put people in touch with those who are likely to have stock for sale. The local goat club can also help with details of local breeders.

Avoid buying horned goats

Reference has already been made to the fact that horns are dangerous! The gentlest of goats can cause injury without meaning to, by a sudden turn of the head. There have been instances of eye loss and other serious injuries where goats have not been disbudded as kids.

Buy from a breeder

It is advisable to buy direct from a breeder, rather than from a third party. A breeder of pure-bred goats will provide details of the goat's parentage, pedigree and registration. (See *Check its Identification*)

Check the health status

Buy from a CAE (Caprine Arthritis Encephalitis) accredited or CAE monitored herd, and one that is also Scrapie monitored. Check that the herd is free from Caseous Lymphadenitis (CL). Copies of guarantees that the herd is regularly tested and free of these conditions are available from the breeder.

UK (holding of birth) ear tag

Herd mark

Individual number

Check its identification

It is also advisable to check that the goat has been vaccinated against clostridial diseases, and is free of parasitic worms. After worming, it should be kept off new pasture for 48 hours. Keeping a new goat in quarantine for about a week is also a good idea. If there are incipient problems, these will tend to show up before animals are introduced to each other.

When ownership of a pure-bred goat is transferred, the Registration Card and a Transfer Form (from the seller) are sent to the BGS with details of the new ownership. (Angora, Boer, Cashmere, English, Bagot and Pygmy goats are registered with their own breed societies). Breed registration is not the same as official DEFRA goat registration .

Parentage

In the UK, a dairy goat with the prefix R to her name is one officially milk-recorded as having given over 1,000kg of milk with over 3% butterfat in a 365 day lactation. A stud male whose mother and father's mother have both qualified in this way, will have the symbol § before his name. Some males also have a dagger prefix, †. This indicates that his mother and his father's mother have both qualified for awards in 24-hour milking competitions at BGS recognised shows. These awards are * or Q* symbols.

Conformation

One of the key factors which indicates a good conformation in a dairy goat is the size of the rumen. Where this is reasonably large, it shows that the goat has a good capacity for roughage or bulky foods. Rumen size is related to her shape which should be that of a wedge or triangle when viewed from the side, from above, or from the front. Her back should be nice and straight with no marked dip in the middle, a feature which could indicate muscular weakness.

Legs should be straight, with the back ones fairly wide apart. The pasterns, or area of leg immediately above the back of the feet, should be straight and not turned inwards. The feet should be neat, with no over-grown hooves.

The head and neck of a dairy goat are fine and neat. There may or may not be tassels, depending on the breed of the goat. These are long, thin appendages hanging from the area at the back and under the jawline.

The eyes should be bright and alert. Eyes, ears, nostrils and vent should be free of discharge. There should be no swollen glands.

The udder of a milking goat is obviously very important. (See Page 15). It should be well attached, indicating that the muscles are in good condition. Any lumps or areas of scar tissue could indicate previous bouts of mastitis and should be investigated. The udder should be smooth and silky to the touch. The ideal shape is spherical, with the two teats pointing slightly forwards. These should taper towards the end and be of a reasonable size for ease of milking. If the teats are over-large, kids may experience difficulty in suckling. (It should be remembered that the udder and teats will enlarge after kidding).

The conformation of the Angora goat is quite different from that of the dairy goat. It is much more rectangular in shape, giving a blockier appearance, more like a sheep than a goat. The legs are shorter and sturdier, with heavier muscular growth. Pure Angoras will have long, lustrous curls of fine, white mohair that is free of coarse, straight hairs (kemp). Further details of breed conformation for the different types of goat are given in the *Breeds* chapter.

Condition

Check the coat and skin to ensure that these are clean and free of external parasites such as lice, mites or ticks. If the coat is coarse and staring, it may be an indication of internal worm infestation. There should be no dry, flaking skin or other sore conditions. It is worth remembering that a goat in full milk production will not be in show condition. Make allowances for those which have been wintering inside; their coats are bound to have lost condition in that time.

Age at which to buy

The choice is between kids, goatlings (young females that have not yet been mated), in-kid goats or milking goats. The smaller goatkeeper would not be wise to consider buying a male of any age, unless there is a special reason such as a shortage of good males in the area, or an interest in breeding. An exception is where spayed males are pets or are to be used as harness goats.

If you buy kids, this has the advantage that they become used to their owner before a possibly difficult period such as milking for the first time is experienced. Goatlings are high-spirited, but again, there is an opportunity for them to become used to their owner before they take their place in the herd. There is less time to wait before they become productive, and many people buy at this age because the tasks such as bottle-feeding and weaning are over. Buying an in-kid doe has its advantages, as long as the sire is known and acceptable. She is normally adaptable, without being too excitable.

Whichever age or type of goat is acquired, it should not be forgotten that the secretary of the local goat society is in an excellent position to help and advise. He or she usually knows who has what goats for sale in the area, and the society frequently has a register of breeders. Such a contact is invaluable.

At the end of its life

An old, infirm or seriously ill goat should be humanely put down by a licensed slaughterer or a vet who will normally arrange for the disposal of the carcase.

DEFRA must be informed.

A British Saanen enjoying some browse material in an outside rack. *(Katie Thear)*

Breeds

Goats come in regularly in the evening and if called, they come, like dogs.
(William Cobbett. Cottage Economy. 1830)

Dairy breeds

The main commercial dairy breeds in Britain are the British Saanen, British Toggenburg, British Alpine and Anglo Nubian, for these are the most productive. However there are other breeds that are kept for a variety of reasons, including an interest in the original breeds on which the commercial strains were based.

British Saanen

The British Saanen was developed in Britain from imported Saanen goats but is bigger and has longer legs. It also has a larger milk yield, making it one of the most widely kept breeds in the UK. The British Goat Society recognises that pure-bred Saanens can be crossed with British Saanens, with the young being registered as British Saanens.

It is a placid-natured goat with a good record of high milk yields and long lactations. The short-haired coat is white, although there may be patches of colour on the skin. The face may be slightly dished or straight in contour and neck tassels may be present or absent.

Saanen

The all-white Saanen originated in the Saane valley in Switzerland. It has been exported to so many countries that it is now the most widely available of the developed breeds. In Switzerland, it is the goat with the best level of milk production. It was introduced to Britain in 1903, with further importations, this time from Holland, taking place in 1922. In 1965, Saanens were again imported from Switzerland. In recent years, semen has also been introduced from Switzerland and Holland.

It is a fairly small breed that is pure white and short-haired, although fringes of longer hair can occur. There may also be neck tassels. The temperament is generally calm and there are good milkers available.

British Toggenburg

The British Toggenburg was developed in Britain from the Toggenburg that came from Switzerland, although it is considerably bigger. The colour can vary from light brown to deeper shades of brown, but with the characteristic Swiss markings of white facial stripes, white legs and white around the tail. The coat is generally short, although there may be fringes of longer hair.

The shape of the face tends to be straighter than the more dish-shaped appearance of the Toggenburg. Neck tassels may be present or absent. It sometimes has a boisterous temperament. Large and friendly, it may need stronger confinement to keep it in one place. Its milk yield is good with a relatively high level of butterfats, making it a good choice for the commercial herd, particularly if yoghurt or cheese production are envisaged.

Toggenburg

The Toggenburg originated in Obertoggenburg in the north-west of Switzerland. It is smaller than the British Toggenburg but has the same brown and white marked coat, although this is usually silky and fringed. It has more of a dished face than the British Toggenburg and the head is distinctively wide across the eyes. Neck tassels may be present.

Introduced into Britain in 1882, with subsequent importations of stock and semen, its attractive appearance and friendly disposition make it ideal for the family. Registered pure-bred Toggenburgs can be crossed with British Toggenburgs, with the progeny being registered as British Toggenburg.

British Alpine

The British Alpine was developed in Britain from French Alpine goats that came to Britain in 1903. It has a striking appearance with a glossy black, short-haired coat that has Swiss markings of white face stripes, white legs and a white tail area. The face may be dished or straight and there may be neck tassels, although these are frequently absent.

Its distinctive colouring often makes it the choice of those interested in pet goats, although its milk yield makes it suitable as a milk provider for the family. It can sometimes be long-legged and a bit rangy.

Anglo-Nubian

Britain has been responsible for developing one of the most popular and distinctive of the goat breeds. The Anglo-Nubian was produced by crossing Indian and Sudanese Nubian goats with indigenous British goats at the turn of the last century. The result is an attractive and productive animal with Roman nose and long, floppy ears.

The quality of its milk is good, with plenty of butterfats and proteins, although it produces less in quantity than, for example, British Saanens and British Toggenburgs. It is often referred to as 'the Jersey of the goat world' and is a good choice for those interested in producing dairy products such as yoghurt, cheese or ice cream.

The Anglo-Nubian is also popular as a family or pet goat and is frequently seen in farm parks and specialist zoos. It has a short-haired, silky coat and is available in a variety of colours, including black, mahogany brown, grey, white and cream. These colours may be single or in mottled patterns. Neck tassels are not allowed under the breed standards.

Golden Guernsey

The little Channel island of Guernsey has given the world the Guernsey cow as well as the Golden Guernsey goat. It really is golden, with silky hair, often long and wavy, and is popular as a small, pet goat for many people. The gold colour can vary from a pale blonde gold to a deep bronze. The breed standards do not allow Swiss marking or neck tassels.

Its milk yield is fairly small, making it unsuitable as a commercial breed, but quite satisfactory as a family milk provider. It has a considerable advantage over some breeds in its hardiness and high roughage diet preference. Its distribution is limited, being confined to Guernsey and mainland Britain. It was first introduced to mainland Britain in 1965.

British Guernsey

The British Guernsey was recognised as a separate breed in 1975. It has been developed by crossing Golden Guernsey males with females of other breeds such as Saanen, over several generations. It is bigger than the Golden Guernsey and the coat is often paler cream in colour. The standards do not allow Swiss markings or neck tassels.

English

Once common in Britain, the indigenous type of goat was in danger of becoming lost because of cross-breeding with imported goats. As a result of a breeding programme instigated by the English Goat Breeders' Association, the English goat now breeds true to type and has its own standard.

Hair length can vary, but is usually longer in the male. The colour is variable, in shades of brown and grey, but with a distinctive dark line along the back called

30

an 'eel stripe'. There are also dark markings on the head, legs and flanks. Swiss markings, as in the Toggenburg and British Alpine, are permitted in the standards but ideally should be absent. Tassels are naturally absent.

It is a hardy and docile breed that produces reasonable amounts of milk without needing large amounts of concentrate foods.

British

British goats are those that are not eligible for inclusion in a breed section recognised by the BGS, although they can be registered with them. In some cases, they may be previously unregistered females that are to be used for a selective breeding programme where 'grading up' to a specific breed status is the aim.

British goats can be of any colour. There are some highly productive and hardy goats in this category, including some in commercial herds. There have also been show champions in this category.

Fibre goats

Angora

Some of the most expensive goats in the world are pure-bred Angoras. They are smaller than dairy goats and produce mohair, a fine lustrous fibre much in demand in the quality textile field. It should not be confused with angora wool, which comes from Angora rabbits. Most goats have double coats, with a soft underdown and coarse outer hairs. Angoras are mostly single-coated with a lustrous fleece that forms ringlets or staples with a spiral twist that gives it style and a crimp that gives it character. The presence of coarse hair, known as kemp, is regarded as a fault.

The pure Angora is a most attractive all-white goat with long ringlets of lustrous hair. Originally bred in Turkey, it was introduced into South Africa in 1838. It arrived in the USA in 1848, Australia in 1853 and Britain in 1881, with a subsequent importation in 1885. However, it was not until 1981, when a consignment of New Zealand Angoras was imported, that a rapidly-developing commercial interest got under way in the UK. Since 1986, the emphasis in Britain has been on the importation of embryo transplants from New Zealand, Australia, Canada and Texas.

Cashmere

The name Cashmere was first used by Europeans to describe goats producing the fine fibre of that name because the trade route for these goats ended in Kashmir. Therefore Kashmir was the place where western traders first saw or heard of the animals, which did not originate there, as some have claimed, but came from the Central Asian mountains, including Tibet, China, Mongolia and Iran. Today, the major producing countries of cashmere are China, Mongolia, Iran, Pakistan and Afghanistan, with China producing the best quality.

There is no fixed breed of goat called the Cashmere. It is essentially a name given to any goats that produce a substantial amount of cashmere fibres. Feral goats do so and native animals have been successfully crossed with imported semen to produce goats that are cashmere-producing. There is some evidence that these crosses are now breeding true.

Cashgora

There is no breed of goat called the Cashgora. The name refers to animals that have been selected from succeeding generations of dairy goats crossed with pure Angora males. Fibre produced by Cashgoras has some features of mohair. There is little commercial demand for it, although home spinners use it.

Meat goats
Boer

Originating in South Africa, the Boer goat is a large white animal with a chestnut brown head. It is primarily a meat producer. An adult male can reach 150kg. It is often used as a terminal sire to cross with dairy goats in order to produce a better meat carcase than a dairy animal would normally produce. They have a fast growth rate (around 200g per day) and are good grazers. The breed was originally introduced to Britain from Europe in the 1980s, with subsequent importations taking place from New Zealand and Canada when direct imports from South Africa were banned.

Other breeds
Bagot

The Bagot goat is a medium-sized black and white goat which was originally the herd animal of the Bagot family. The original stock is said to have been given to them by Richard II. It has a history going back at least 600 years, and is found in private zoos and wildlife parks. It is very similar to the Schwarzhal goat of Switzerland, and is a horned, long-haired goat with a characteristic colour pattern. The front part of the body, from nose to shoulder, is completely black, while the rest of the body is white. Previous crossings have resulted in variations to this pattern. The Bagot Goat Breed Society maintains a list of all the pure breeding stock.

Pygmy

This little African goat has become popular in children's zoos and farm parks in Britain. It is also the choice of many people who like goats as pets or as show animals. The Pygmy Goat Society looks after their interests.

There are basically four types of dwarf goat in Africa, although there are many local variations. These are West African, Southern Sudanese, Somali and Small East African. The type which has been most distributed in Europe is the West African. In these countries it is generally referred to as the African Pygmy or just Pygmy. It is around 37-45 cm at the shoulder, cobby in shape and short-legged. It is commonly dark brown in colour, although black, white and brown variations and patternings are to be found.

Those who keep them find that a small garden shed with attached dog run is quite adequate. There are several known instances of Pygmy goats adapting well to suburban life. They can be trained to use a collar and lead, allowing themselves to be taken for daily walks. The average female will give about 150ml of milk a day.

Harness

Any breed and sex of goat can be trained as a harness animal, but the Harness Goat Society recommends that hornless, castrated males are the most suitable.

Feral goats

There are still populations of wild, feral goats in the British Isles. The old Welsh goat, for example, provides the mascot for the Welsh Guards. There are Scottish and Irish goats, as well as those indigenous to Scandinavia and Holland. All the ancient, feral groups of Northern Europe are similar in appearance. The British Feral Goat Research Group monitors their status.

Housing

There's no place like home.
(Traditional song)

Goats need housing which is dry, well ventilated and free of draughts. There are purpose-made houses available, but many people adapt existing buildings. Depending on the scale and number of goats, these may be stables, piggeries, garages or other outbuildings.

A garden shed can be adapted for a couple of goats and, in the case of Pygmy goats, a large dog kennel and run will suffice. All lend themselves to goat occupation with a little imagination and expertise. The important factor is that the completed house should suit the goats as well as the goatkeeper.

Unless the occupants are the Pygmy breed, a minimum height of 3m is needed, if air is to circulate effectively. Larger houses will be higher (see photo left). Good ventilation is assured by a combination of ridge ventilation and side inlet. This could be a stable-type door with the top half open, or a hopper-type window which opens inwards from the top. If goats are able to reach this, the glass will either need to be removed, or protected with wire mesh. A small house such as a garden shed will have adequate ventilation from the door, window and ridge.

The key factor is that humidity should not exceed 75% and should ideally be around 60 - 65%. Small humidity meters or hygrometers are available in most garden centres and it is a good idea to put one of these in the goathouse (out of reach of the goats which will otherwise regard it as a tempting morsel).

Walls may be of wood, brick, stone or concrete blocks. All are suitable, but breeze blocks should not be used for external walls because they are porous and let in damp.

Heavy duty roofing felt with bitumen is effective in deterring leaks and is widely used in the roofing of small outbuildings. Corrugated iron is strong but has the disadvantage of being cold in winter and far too hot in summer. Modern materials such as Onduline or plasticised steel are lightweight yet effective, enabling skylights to be inserted which provide light and ventilation.

Electric light is not essential in the goat house, but it is certainly useful, particularly on nightly visits when a goat may be kidding or where there is some other emergency. It is relatively easy and inexpensive to extend an electricity supply in this way, and it more than repays itself in terms of convenience. If the goat enterprise begins in a small way it is always appropriate to look towards future expansion.

Inside a house for a herd of British Toggenburg goats. It has natural and electric light and the floor is concreted. Each goat has her own strawed pen equipped with an internal hayrack on the left and an outside drinker on the right. The goats can see each other, which is appropriate for herd animals. There is a door at each end of the house, one for entering and the other for going out. *(Katie Thear)*

Communally housed dairy goats. (Katie Thear)

The floor of the house is just as important as the roof and walls. An earth-rammed floor is usually unsuitable because rats can burrow in. Bricks, tiles or concrete exclude them effectively. If laying a floor, do ensure that there is a slight slope down towards the door; it makes cleaning so much easier. A larger goathouse will usually have a drainage channel for this purpose.

Score marks in the concrete provide a foothold to prevent slipping, while a sealant stops dustiness and facilitates cleaning.

Fibre-producing goats are frequently kept in housing of the Yorkshire boarding type. This is a building which has solid walls up to around 1.3m in height. The rest of the walls are made of wooden slats arranged vertically, but with ventilation gaps. Insulated polythene housing is also frequently used for fibre goats and as grazing protection for dairy goat herds while out on range.

Goat Housing

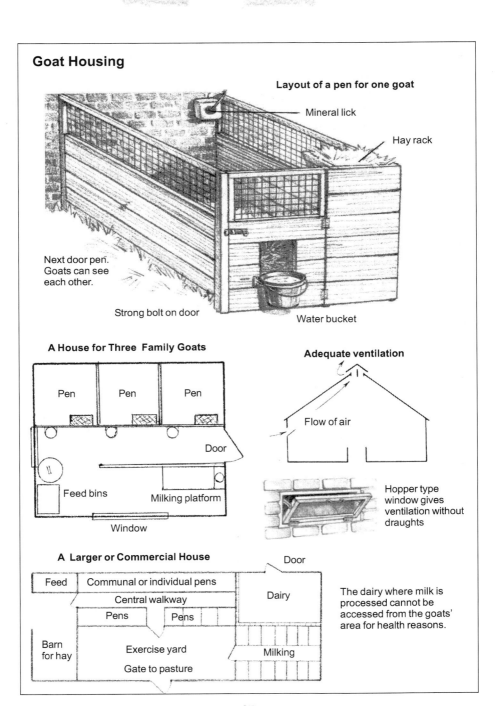

Layout of a pen for one goat

Mineral lick

Hay rack

Next door pen. Goats can see each other.

Strong bolt on door

Water bucket

A House for Three Family Goats

Pen   Pen   Pen

Door

Feed bins

Milking platform

Window

Adequate ventilation

Flow of air

Hopper type window gives ventilation without draughts

A Larger or Commercial House

Door

Feed	Communal or individual pens	Dairy
Central walkway	
Pens	Pens	
Barn for hay	Exercise yard	Milking
Gate to pasture	

The dairy where milk is processed cannot be accessed from the goats' area for health reasons.

Penning

You need to decide at an early stage whether to have individual pens for the goats or to have communal housing. The penning system is where the house is divided into a number of individual pens so that each goat has her own quarters. Communal housing is where they are together in one or more large areas: it is generally used in larger enterprises, and a popular system is to have a central path down the middle of the house, with a communal area on either side. This path is ideally wide enough for a small tractor.

Smaller enterprises tend to favour individual penning. This is more labour-intensive, but with fewer goats labour is not a major factor, and penning does have its advantages. Where a goat is off-colour, for example, it is possible to isolate her where she will not be bothered, until she has had time to recover.

It is possible to buy individual wooden pens, with the purchase including the cost of installation. Alternatively, they are not difficult to construct, but they do need to be strong and well-built. As goats are gregarious herd animals, it is important that they are able to see each other from their pens. One way of achieving this is to use wooden railings covered with Weldmesh panels.

A warmer alternative is to have solid boarding for the bottom section with mesh panels above. The height of the pen needs to be at least 1.3m. Sheep hurdles can also be used to make individual pens. These interlock in any required combination and include gate sections which are fitted as necessary. They are also useful if an emergency pen is required. A fully-grown goat requires a pen at least 1.8 x 1.3m, allowing her to turn round without difficulty.

Fixtures and fittings

Individual pens and communal sleeping areas need straw as floor litter. This material is both warm and effective in absorbing droppings, but requires regular cleaning or 'mucking out'. It can be stacked in a covered heap to rot down until ready for use as a garden fertiliser. (See Page 126).

Each pen needs a hayrack, placed at a comfortable height for the goat to help herself. Ones with lids are better because goats are wasteful of hay, pulling out more than they need and then dropping it. They are fastidious creatures and will refuse to eat hay once it has been on the ground.

It is more convenient for the goat-keeper if the hayrack can be filled from the outside, without having to open the door and enter the pen. Hay nets of the sort

Communally housed dairy goats. (Katie Thear)

used by horses are not recommended for goats, which can easily become entangled in them, and cases of strangulation have been known.

Bucket holders attached to the outside of the pen will also allow the water buckets to be filled from the passageway. Most goatkeepers do not have a feed bucket attached to the pen, preferring to make it available in the milking area instead. This ensures that milking proceeds in a calm and contented atmosphere while the goats are busy eating. The hayrack, with its share of hay, is an acceptable alternative to the feed bucket as far as the goat is concerned, as long as she has her ration of concentrates elsewhere. A water bucket is essential, however, for water should be available at all times. If the buckets and holders are placed outside the pen, it is, of course, essential to have gaps through which the goat can reach them.

Goats need access to salt and mineral licks to ensure that they do not suffer from mineral deficiencies. These are available as blocks which are hung in a convenient position. The animal then licks it whenever it feels the need to do so. The pen is a convenient place to position it, but avoid having too long a piece of twine to suspend it. Again, it is the danger of entanglement which needs to be borne in mind. Where goats are housed communally they will not need individual

39

hayracks and buckets. As a rough guide, each goat will need 50cm of rack or trough space, as long as there is no bullying.

Large herds usually have an automatic water system with a pipeline unit fed from a central tank. The exit points of the pipeline are either into troughs or nipple units. The animals soon learn to drink from the nipples, and these do save a lot of waste. On a small scale, an automatic system is not necessary. The time taken to refill the buckets twice a day is not excessive.

Problems can arise in winter, when the water in the buckets may freeze, and buckets need far more frequent attention; but this ought not to happen if the house is insulated.

The minimum temperature for a goathouse for adult goats should be 6°C, and the maximum should be 27°C. Kids require a minimum of 12°C, but they are normally housed together and so help to keep each other warm. Goats do generate a considerable amount of heat and the commercial herd which is housed communally may have less to fear from cold than the small herd of individually housed domestic goats. Maximum and minimum thermometers, which show the highest daily temperature as well as the lowest night temperature, are widely available. It is a good idea to place one in the goathouse, well out of reach of inquisitive caprine noses.

Hay and feed storage

Hay should be stored in a dry, airy place that is in a separate area from the goathouse or pens because it quickly absorbs smells. Straw bales will also be needed for bedding. Wooden pallets on the floor keep the bales clear of the ground. Alternatively, use planks laid on bricks.

Concentrate feeds need to be in secure bins so that rodents are not able to gain access. They need to have secure lids so that any goat which manages to escape and find its way into the feed storage area is foiled in its attempts at gluttony. This is important, for an animal which does feed in this way can die as a result of overfeeding. A convenient way of measuring out the concentrates is to use a metal scoop with a handle.

Other buildings, depending on the type of goats and on the nature of the enterprise, include the male's house, a milking area and a dairying area. These are discussed in the appropriate chapters later in the book.

Goats Outside

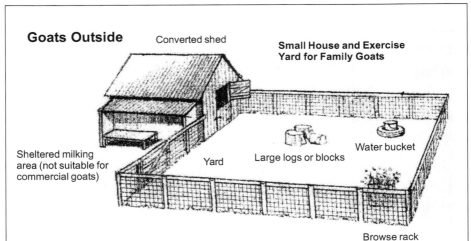

Converted shed

Small House and Exercise Yard for Family Goats

Sheltered milking area (not suitable for commercial goats)

Yard

Large logs or blocks

Water bucket

Browse rack

Field Shelters

Boarded

Polythene housing with reinforced walls

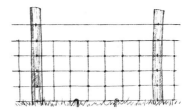

Pig netting is strong but needs an extra strand of wire across the top

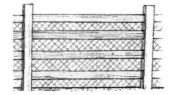

Post and rail fencing should be covered with netting to stop kids squeezing through

Water buckets

Bucket with wall support

Pronged support for pasture use

Tyre support

Feed storage

Goats Outside

Tomorrow to fresh fields and pastures new.
(Paradise Lost. Milton)

There are essentially three systems of management when it comes to goats. These are *free-range, controlled grazing* and *zero-grazing*. The scale of operations may vary, but the basic principles remain the same, so this information is relevant to all goat-keepers, whether they own a couple of pet goats or whether their herd is a large commercial one.

Free-range This means that the goats are completely unrestricted and are able to select their browsing areas over a wide range of terrain. Most goats are unlikely to have such freedom unless they are feral, or their owners happen to live in extensive moorland or mountainous areas.

Controlled grazing This system is where goats are allowed access to certain carefully-controlled areas of pasture or scrubland on a temporary basis, usually being moved on to new areas in sequence. This prevents overuse of the land and avoids a build-up of parasites.

Zero-grazing This is literally what it says; the goats have no grazing at all, and all food must be brought to them in their stalls or exercise yard.

Most goats are kept under a system which is a mixture of controlled grazing and zero-grazing. In Britain, for example, the cold winters in northerly and easterly regions make it necessary for many goats to be stall-fed for most of the winter. Once the weather improves, they are able to switch to a system of controlled grazing outside.

Some goatkeepers prefer to keep their land to grow hay, not allowing their goats to go on it at all. Instead, the animals are stall-fed and exercised in yards. One of the great advantages of this system is that such goats are usually free of internal worms. Their confinement to yards also results in more effective wearing-down of their nails, reducing the need for frequent foot-trimming, although this will still be necessary. Whatever system is followed, the question of outdoor confinement is relevant.

The exercise yard

Where extensive grazing is available, as for example in a field or paddock, goats will have sufficient exercise and browsing areas. Those in more confined conditions need an enclosed area where they can run freely once out of their pens. It is here

These goats have a moveable rack for browse material and can run to the shelter on the left if it rains. The hedge is a good windbreak and is also protected by fencing. *(Katie Thear)*

that a scrambling area is useful; arrange logs or piled up paving stones to provide different levels for their 'mountain climbing'.

The walls of the yard can be of any material which is strong enough to confine goats. This could be brick, blocks or post and wire netting fencing, and needs to be at least 1.3m high.

The ideal yard surface is concrete or flagstones, although rammed earth is suitable. A hard surface can be hosed down easily, with the run-off going into a drainage channel and drain. Concreted areas should always be scored to prevent slipping. The yard will need a water bucket or trough. If it is not possible to attach a bucket to the fencing or wall, a good alternative is to place it in a rubber tyre. This will ensure that it is not knocked over.

A hayrack is necessary to hold the hay or other roughage, and if this is in a corner of the yard it may be possible to put a partial roof over the rack so that it will not get wet in a sudden shower of rain. This also gives the goats a sheltered area to run to whenever there is a shower.

Many larger goat concerns also have yards, not necessarily because they are short of browsing land, but because it is useful as a general marshalling area. For example, when the goats are to be milked, it may be more convenient to collect them together before leading them as a group into the milking area.

43

Routine tasks such as foot trimming or worming may also be more conveniently performed in a yard, while fibre goats can be shorn there. In severe weather, outdoor browsing may not be possible at all and a yard is a good alternative, particularly if one area of it is covered over.

Perimeter fencing

It is no good relying on the traditionally laid stockproof hedge, which is effective for cattle and sheep. Goats will push and eat their way through it. Their mouths can tackle brambles and briars with impunity. If the Prince had been accompanied by a goat when he made his way to Sleeping Beauty's palace in the thorny wood, he would not have needed his hacking sword.

As a general rule, a 1.3m fence will contain most goats, although the occasional high-spirited goatling may scale it. A satisfactory fence is made by erecting sturdy fence posts, about 3m apart, with sheep or pig netting filling the gaps. The posts will need to be braced at the corners for strength. Once a post begins to develop a lean, the goats will push against it until it provides a handy stepping stone to freedom.

Sheep and pig netting is not quite high enough, so an extra strand of wire will need to be run above it. This could be electrified, if necessary. Barbed wire should be avoided for it can inflict cruel wounds, and many people would like to see its use banned in the countryside.

Chestnut paling fences are not suitable for goats. They can push their way through them, and the sharp tops of the palings can cause serious damage if a scrambling goat should become impaled (it has happened). If such a fence is already in existence, it can be made safe by covering it with wire netting and folding this over the top. Post-and-rail fences, of the type used for horses, are suitable, as long as the gaps are filled with netting. If not, kids can squeeze through, while older goats will use the rails as a conveniently-placed ladder.

Electric fencing

The energising unit for electric fencing can be mains-operated, or battery-run. If there is an existing perimeter fence or hedge which merely needs supplementing, then possibly one or two strands may be sufficient. Sheep or pig netting, which requires an extra strand across the top to provide sufficient height, could have this strand electrified. Alternatively, a one or two-strand electric fence could be erected just in front of the existing barrier.

Electric fencing confining a herd of English goats. *(English Goat Breeders' Association)*

The wires need to be tensioned correctly, otherwise they will tend to sag. It is much easier for two people to erect and tension the wires, rather than for one person to struggle alone. All the equipment and accessories for erecting the fences are available from the manufacturers, and their advice is useful.

Grass must be kept short where an electric fence is erected, otherwise the growth will earth the current and the fence ceases to function.

Training the goats

It is hard to generalise about ways of teaching goats about electric fencing because circumstances and individual animals vary so much, but you should initially teach them what the fence can do, rather than simply putting it up, turning the goats out and leaving them to find out the hard way. You will need sensitivity and judgement, for if you merely haul the animal up to the fence you may frighten her badly and possibly harm your relationship with her.

The best approach is to try and lead the animal towards the fence, without pushing her. At the instant she receives a shock shout 'No!' as firmly as possible and then push her away. Immediately make a great fuss of the goat, once she is well away from the fence, stroking and talking to her, perhaps giving her a tit-bit to reassure her. It is a time-consuming process, but it is worth it.

Grazing shelters

Free-ranging goats need shelter to which they can run when rain threatens. A simple three-sided and open-fronted structure is quite adequate. For a small number of goats, this could be a home-made building, using stout poles and corrugated iron sheets. Disused sheds or poultry houses can be adapted and turned into goat shelters. Any glass should be removed from windows, as well as perches, nest-boxes and so on. Moveable sheep shelters made of plastic are worth considering. These are pegged into the ground and are easily transportable. When not in use, they can be stacked together for storing.

For a larger number of goats, polythene housing makes a suitable grazing shelter. The bottom half of the wall is normally reinforced with boards and plastic netting or some other suitable material. An alternative is to use wooden buildings with Yorkshire boarding walls.

Pasture

There are two kinds of pasture: permanent which is never ploughed up and temporary where the land is periodically ploughed up and resown with a special seed mixture or ley. The mixture suitable for goats is not necessarily that which is appropriate for sheep, cattle or horses.

Specialist suppliers have ley mixtures for goats. A suitable mixture might be the following:

> Perennial ryegrass, Timothy, Red clover, Wild white clover, Ribgrass plantain, Yarrow, Chicory, Burnet, Sheep's parsley, Sorrel, Alsike clover, Dandelion

This is but one suggestion. Many different mixtures are available, and the seedsman will have his own suggestions to make in the light of specific local soil conditions. Most will make up mixtures to your specification.

Perennial ryegrass is a highly productive grass suitable for a wide range of conditions, while timothy is an adaptable grass which grows more slowly, providing slightly later grazing than the ryegrass. The red and white clovers are legumes, able to 'fix' nitrogen from the air into their root nodules, thereby increasing the overall nitrogen content of the soil. Alsike is a developed strain of white clover. The remaining plants are all broad-leaved and contain calcium, phosphorus, magnesium and cobalt.

Goats need a wide range of minerals in their diet. In the wild, they are able to obtain them by ranging over a considerable expanse of terrain, selectively browsing over a variety of herbage. In more confined, domesticated conditions they have less choice. One of the ways in which the variety can be widened for them is to provide pasture containing a selection of suitable plants.

Grasses are useful sources of protein, carbohydrates and vitamins, but their mineral content is fairly limited. It is the deeper-rooted broad-leaved plants which provide these. The deep roots are able to penetrate to greater depths, bringing up a wider selection of minerals. These plants, from the point of view of goats, are essential reservoirs of the elements that they need. A good pasture for goats is therefore one which contains grasses and mineral rich, broad-leaved plants.

If the land is to have a new ley mixture, the area is ploughed over in the autumn and the soil tested to see what the lime and fertiliser requirements are likely to be. You can either do this yourself with a farm-sized soil testing kit, or ask a specialist to do it. A suitable pH value is 6.4. After the land has been ploughed and, if necessary, limed in the autumn, it is harrowed to break down the large particles in the early spring. Then the seed mixture is sown immediately after that.

In two to three months, the pasture will be ready for light grazing. As long as grazing is not too heavy, the cropping action of the goats will help to thicken it, the principle being that as plants are grazed down they produce more shoots.

Pasture should be 'topped' if it gets too long, particularly if the flower heads begin to appear. Doing this will not only maintain the nutrient levels which would otherwise be dispersed by the flowering, but stimulates fresh growth for the goats. If a farm tractor with cutter is not available you can do it yourself with a ride-on garden tractor, with the blades set at maximum height.

Rotational grazing

The best way to make pasture available is to divide it up so that it is used in rotation. This prevents over-use of the land and prevents a build-up of parasites. The 'resting' area can have other livestock such as cattle to follow, but it is best to avoid sheep for they and goats share many of the same parasites and diseases.

Any pasture which is scheduled for hay cutting should not have goats or any other livestock grazing on it, even for a short time. Once the hay is cut and carried, and the grass has begun to grow again, they can have access.

Dairy goats browsing and free-ranging on a Spanish hillside. *(Katie Thear)*

Making your own hay

The grass is cut at the leafy stage, just before flowering. At this time its nutrient levels are at their peak. Equipment includes a tractor, cutter and baler. If these are not available, a contractor can be hired to do it. A garden tractor with the blades set fairly high is perfectly good for cutting hay on a small scale. Cutting by hand with a scythe is another option, but it is hard work and requires skill.

After cutting, the grass is left until the surface is dry, and then turned over. On a small scale, tripods are commonly used for drying hay. The advantage of this system is that there is plenty of air around it which is conducive to rapid drying. If it does rain, the water runs down rather than soaking through.

Once the hay is completely dry, it can be gathered up into a cart and taken to its storage place. The ideal is to have it baled. On a small scale this is not possible, unless you are prepared to spend time stuffing it into a container and tying it up, as shown in the diagram on the right. Most small goatkeepers will be buying in hay and it is important to check its quality. Further details are on page 53.

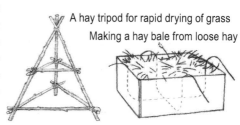

A hay tripod for rapid drying of grass

Making a hay bale from loose hay

48

Feeding

I should prefer a goat, which is hardier and much more domestic.
(Cottage Economy. William Cobbett. 1830)

The domestic goat requires a balance between roughage and concentrates in the diet. *Roughage* is the term for bulk foods such as hay, grass, twiggy growth and herbage generally. *Concentrates* are foods such as cereals and soya bean meal which have comparatively high nutritional values in relation to their volume. The goat is a ruminant with a digestive system adapted to dealing with large quantities of bulk foods from browsing. It is essential that a correct balance is maintained between roughage and concentrates. Too much concentrates at the expense of bulk foods will interfere with the workings of the rumen and cause digestive problems.

The rumen is just one area of a four-chambered stomach (see page 18). Bulk foods are chewed quickly and when swallowed go into the reticulum and rumen to be broken down. This occurs by combination of fermentation and rumination. Rumen bacteria bring about the process of fermentation, while rumination occurs when large pieces of roughage are regurgitated and chewed again, a process referred to as 'chewing the cud'.

Once the pieces are small enough they are swallowed and passed through the omasum, or filtering compartment, into the abomasum, or true stomach. Any pieces which fail to get through the filter go back again for another chew.

From the abomasum, the process continues along the normal lines for most mammals. In the small intestine nutrients are absorbed into the blood stream through the blood capillaries. The blood then transports them to all the body cells which rely on them for survival and growth. Any unusable material continues to the large intestine, or colon, where water is extracted, leaving the relatively dry faeces to be expelled at the anus. Surplus water is taken to the kidneys whose filtering action extracts impurities, which are expelled as urine.

Maintenance and production

It is useful to think of the goat's diet in terms of maintenance and production. A maintenance ration is one which provides for the basic needs of the body and its workings. A production ration caters for the extras like the production of milk, meat or fibre. As an example, the following gives a recommended daily ration (given in two feeds) for an average dairy goat.

Maintenance ration	**Production ration** (for every 1 litre milk)
2kg hay 500g of concentrates	300g hay 200g of concentrates

This ration is obviously a generalisation because individual goats will vary in their appetite and needs, and who ever heard of an average goat? But it does give a general indication which may be helpful. It is important to remember that the rumen with its roughage always comes first.

Regardless of the quantity of milk, the amount of concentrate for a dairy goat should not normally exceed 1.8 kg a day, otherwise the balance between roughage and concentrate is distorted, with possible disturbances to the rumen.

Elements of the diet
Hay

As hay is such an important part of the goat's diet, it needs to be the best quality available. It maintains optimum conditions for the rumen bacteria to operate in, and provides the fibrous texture necessary to balance soft, lush growth in the early part of the year. A commonly held belief is that any old hay will do for goats, and the rougher the better. The belief no doubt originated from the idea that because goats eat weeds they must therefore prefer rough grass. It is quite untrue!

Goats eat a wide range of different herbage. They are highly selective eaters. When it comes to a cheap bale of hay and a good quality bale of hay, they will take the quality one. Cheap hay is cheap for good reasons. It was probably cut late in the year so its nutritional value will be relatively low.

The best hay is cut when the pasture is at its most leafy, but just before flowering. The nutritional value at this time is high, and as long as cutting, drying and baling take place quickly, comparatively little of it is lost. A good bale of hay is green rather than yellow, and has a high proportion of leaf in relation to coarse stem. The smell should be that of new-mown hay without any mustiness. The latter indicates dampness and mouldiness which would make it not only unpalatable but possibly dangerous.

The presence of seeds in a bale suggests that it was cut after flowering, not before, so the nutritional value is lower than it could be. Buying cheap hay is an expensive mistake. The best and most economic way of buying it is direct from the farm, and in bulk, with sufficient to last for the whole year. Storage space is needed; the ideal is a hay barn or large shed which will provide the dry, airy conditions necessary.

Young British Alpine eating hay. *(Katie Thear)*

Concentrates

Concentrates are what the term implies, foods which are in denser form than roughage, and having a higher nutritional value packed into less space. They include the cereals such as oats, barley, wheat and maize, and the pulses such as peas and beans. They are never served whole for they would be too indigestible. They are processed or flaked, chopped, kibbled or crushed and then made up as a concentrate ration. A typical mixture ration might be:

1 part flaked maize: 1 part rolled oats: 1 part bran: 1 part soya bean meal

If a goat was being fed a basic ration of hay a day, the above mixture would provide her concentrate ration. But it could still not be regarded as a complete diet. With the levels of production that are expected of dairy goats in terms of milk and of fibre goats for their fibre, there also needs to be a feed supplement of minerals, trace elements and vitamins. Some of these will be in the existing hay and concentrates, others will come from green food and roots. They can also be added to the concentrate ration as ready-made supplements.

A proprietary coarse goat ration (coarse mix) is therefore a mixture of concentrates with minerals, vitamins and trace elements added. A number of

Angora goats eating a concentrate ration. They are normally left horned. *(Katie Thear)*

feed manufacturers produce these ready-formulated, and most people will buy these concentrate feeds already mixed. Some will prefer to buy the ingredients separately and mix their own. This is economic only if you have bulk storage and mixing facilities. The main concentrate feeds are as follows:

Wheat: Widely available and relatively cheap, wheat must be crushed or clipped before it is utilised in a goat mix. It must not be fed to excess.

Bran: This is the fibrous, outer part of wheat and a valuable source of fibre and of Vitamin B. An excess can be disruptive because of its laxative properties.

Oats: Crushed or rolled oats are preferable because they are easier to digest than whole oats, although they do not store as well.

Barley: This is often used in winter rations because of its heating effect, but an excess can cause problems. Use small quantities only.

Maize: As flaked maize which has been cooked, rolled and dried, it is in an ideal form for goat mixtures. They love it, often picking out these bits first.

Soya bean: A rich source of protein but low in fibre.

Oilseed cake/meal: This is the left-over compressed product from the extraction of oils for human use. Rich in protein and energy value, its main drawback is that it does not store for long without going mouldy.

Peas and beans: These are high protein foods but need to be processed, coarsely ground or kibbled before use.

A goat's need for protein in relation to carbohydrates is in the relation of around 15% to 65%. There is more protein in pasture in spring and summer, so the protein levels can be adjusted accordingly.

Minerals

Minerals which are lost in daily milk production have to be replaced. The most important ones are calcium, phosphorus, magnesium, iodine, cobalt, copper and sodium. They are usually made available in a concentrate mix or as an added supplement. Many are found in cereals, grasses and legumes, as well as in wild plants such as nettles, plantains, sorrel, dandelion, chicory and yarrow.

Vitamins

Goats are unlikely to suffer from vitamin deficiencies if they have pasture, sunlight, hay, concentrates and a good mineral and vitamin supplement in the diet. The availability of fodder crops and wild foods will also increase their choice. They are found in grasses, grains, maize, peas, beans, carrots, comfrey, kale and other green foods.

Silage

Silage is produced when grass and other green plants are excluded from air by being compressed in a covered heap. In these anaerobic conditions, bacteria producing lactic acid get to work, and the acid has a 'pickling' effect on the plant material. To produce it properly, it must be done on a large scale, and although people have tried to make it by using small plastic sacks, the results have not been good. The problem is one of efficient compression and sealing to exclude air. If it is not done properly, there is a risk of soil-borne disease.

Access to fresh water is needed at all times, inside and out. *(Katie Thear)*

Some goatkeepers buy big-bale silage or haylage, but machinery is needed to move them. Silaged lucerne with molasses is also available in fairly small quantities. The value of silage is as a winter feed, although it must be fed with discretion, ensuring that it comes secondary to hay. Most small goatkeepers are able to manage very well without silage.

Fodder crops

Some goatkeepers grow vegetable crops for their goats. Depending on the scale, these will either be grown in a field or in a kitchen garden.

Kale Kale can be cut as needed and put in racks. It is important not to overfeed for two reasons: an excess can bloat the animals, as well as 'lock up' supplies of iodine in the diet, leading to goitre.

Carrots Store in sand, then wash before feeding. Cut extra large ones in case goats choke on them.

54

Comfrey Another permanent crop, comfrey is extremely deep-rooted, bringing up huge reserves of minerals. It can be fed green or cut and dried as hay, but, beware handling it too much. Some people are allergic to its hairy leaves.

Lucerne This is a useful crop for feeding green or cut as hay. It does best in mild areas. Lucerne nuts are also available but are often expensive to buy.

Sugar beet pulp This should be soaked for 3-4 hours. It can be fed separately to provide variation in the diet. Avoid giving it to males if there is a risk of urinary blockage.

Wild plants

There is a whole range of wild foods which can be gathered from unsprayed hedgerows, or from the wilder corners of the garden. They are good sources of fibrous material, minerals and vitamins, as well as being a source of interest. As a general rule, most deciduous trees are safe, but avoid evergreens. If in doubt as to identification, consult a book such as *British Poisonous Plants*.

Plants which are generally popular with goats include the following:

> Bramble, Briar rose, Crab apple, Elder, Elm, Hawthorn, Hazel, Lime, Chickweed, Clovers, Dandelion, Docks, Fat hen, Ivy (not berries), Knapweed, Plantains, Thistles, Vetches, Nettles (young).

Poisonous plants

There are also plants which are poisonous and should be avoided. It is difficult to draw a neat line and say that everything listed on one side is good to eat, while those on the other side are poisonous. Life is rarely that simple. There has been insufficient research to indicate precisely what plants are toxic, and if so, to what degree? This list is therefore confined to particularly toxic plants:

> Autumn crocus, Bracken, Bryony, Cuckoo pint, Evergreen trees, Foxgloves, Hemlock, Laburnum, Nightshades, Potato haulms, Privet, Ragwort, Rhubarb leaves, Rhododendron, Thornapple, Tomato haulms, Yew.

A group of young British Toggenburgs from a commercial herd out on pasture. *(Katie Thear)*

Water

I once had a goat that never seemed to drink anything. Then she kidded and before I knew where I was, I was constantly filling and refilling her bucket. Relative needs for water do fluctuate, depending on bodily needs, amount of succulent foods eaten and general environmental conditions. It is important to have water there at all times, because even when little or nothing appears to be drunk, it is probably being sampled when needed. The water should be clean, fresh and changed daily. It is particularly important that the male is encouraged to drink if there are any signs of urinary blockage. Males have a tendency to develop stones. If you live in an area of hard water, it is a good idea to give rain water, unless the domestic water supply is fitted with a water softener.

Feeding practice

Nutritional needs change over the year, not only because more of one type of food, such as protein, will be in pasture in the summer, but because the goat itself may have different demands. A goat drying off during pregnancy will need less protein for a time, but she must then have an increase to cater for the growing kids. A goat kept for its coat will differ from a dairy animal in its requirements. These differing needs are covered in the appropriate chapters but for the average milking goat, a typical routine might be as follows:

- Good morning goats!
- Milkers to milking area; fed half daily concentrate ration while being milked.
- Non-milkers fed concentrates in their pens.
- All goats to pasture or to exercise yard (water, hay/browse and shelter).
- Regular checks to make sure all is well during the day.
- Milkers returned for second milking and given the rest of their concentrates.
- Non-milkers returned to their pens and given hay and water.
- Milkers returned to their pens and given hay and water.
- Good night goats!

In winter, or inclement weather, this routine will vary, with more browse food and hay to make up for the lack of grazing. It is but one of many alternatives and goatkeepers will quickly establish what system is the most convenient for them and their goats. What matters is that, whatever the routine, the goats have a balanced diet and the routine is not subject to sudden, drastic changes.

Details of feeding at different stages and for different types of goats are to be found in the appropriate chapters.

Goat with six week old kids. *(Katie Thear)*

Breeding

Oes gafr eto? (Is there another goat?)
(Traditional Welsh song)

Goats breed at definite times of the year, with the onset of oestrus or the breeding cycle being controlled by hormonal action. This, in turn, is affected by the decrease in the amount of light in late summer. As a result, the onset of the breeding cycle takes place in autumn. The average gestation period is 150 days, although this can vary between 142—162 days, depending on type and size of goat, hereditary factors and on other factors which may relate to the condition of the individual goat.

Reasons for breeding

- **To ensure a milk supply** Once a goat has kidded she will produce a regular supply of milk. There are incidences of 'maiden milkers', or of goats lactating without ever having kidded, but the volume is usually fairly low.

- **For future herd replacements** Breed the best possible kids as replacements. A registered male with the appropriate characteristics that are required is the best choice. The characteristics will vary, depending on the individual enterprise, but if it is for progeny with a good milking potential, a male with a record of such potential in his family line is obviously the one to choose. Ask the secretary of the local goat society or of the individual breed society.

- **To produce kids for meat** On a small scale, the most likely source of goat meat is the unwanted male kid. On a larger scale, a breed such as the Boer goat will provide animals that are more suitable for meat production. It is quite common to cross dairy goats with a Boer male so that the progeny can be reared for meat while the female is brought back into lactation.

- **To produce kids for sale** There has to be a demand to make this worthwhile. It is generally true that the best of its kind will always sell. Applying this principle to goats, only the best quality pedigree goats should be aimed for.

Whatever the reasons are for choosing to go in for goat breeding, it is important to choose breeding animals which are in tip-top condition. Having them blood-tested to ensure freedom from inheritable diseases and from Caprine Arthritis Encephalitis is essential. Many goat studs will not allow untested goats on to their premises. From the applicant's point of view it is equally desirable that the stud male is known to be blood-tested.

Age at which to breed

Commercial goatkeepers breed their goats in their first year: This means that a kid born at the turn of the year will be mated in the autumn for kidding in the spring. For this, she will need to be well-grown and in good condition.

Smaller goatkeepers, who do not have the same commercial pressures, tend to leave their goats until they are 18 months old before they are mated, so that kidding normally takes place around the age of two years old. It is also the practice of many goatkeepers to confine kiddings to once every two years. If you have two female goats, you may be able to have them kidding alternately, so that as one is declining as a milk producer, the other is ready to take over when she kids. Unlike cows, which produce milk for a specified period of around nine months, a good goat will continue to lactate for two years, or even longer. This allows them to be 'run through' as winter milk suppliers. Commercial producers tend to kid most of their goats each year, with the kidding period extended over as wide a range as possible. Early kiddings are particularly important to them because the 'staggered' kidding ensures that overall milk supplies do not fluctuate throughout the year.

The male goat

It is usually unnecessary for those with few goats to keep a male. If the decision is taken to keep one, then appropriate conditions must be provided. He will need to be hornless for safety reasons, and have his own house and concrete exercise yard. Housing, penning and fencing must be substantial and well built. A male goat is strong and can be destructive. A suitable arrangement is to have a passageway next to the pen so that food and water can be given, without having to go in. If the pen has a second door opening on to an exercise yard, it is a good idea to have the facility of opening that door without having to go into the yard. When the pen needs cleaning, close the yard door from the pen once he is outside. When the yard needs cleaning, you can shut him in the pen.

It is not necessary for most goatkeepers to keep a male. *(English Goat Breeders' Association)*

Some breeders allow a castrate to share his quarters, so that he has a companion, but it needs to be one that he has grown up with so that there is no fighting. The other aspect worth remembering is that in the breeding season the male smells in a most objectionable manner. It is essential to wear an overall kept purely for the purpose before going to his house. The smell is particularly pervasive and his house should be placed well away from a dwelling.

If a male is being reared from a kid to adulthood for stud purposes, check that the testicles are properly descended. He should have up to 2 litres of milk every day, starting with small amounts and gradually increasing. Start with four feeds, reducing to three. Weaning normally takes place from the age of six months onwards and some goatkeepers continue to give him a little milk right through his first winter. Hay should be available to appetite, with concentrates at around 225g a day initially, gradually increasing to 500g, then to 1.5kg, depending on his size.

Grazing and most green foods, together with a variety of branches, can be given, but avoid root crops such as mangolds, or kale and sugar beet pulp. These can lead to urinary blockage problems. A mineral and salt lick should be placed in his house. The drinking water may need to be changed very frequently because of the male's tendency to urinate all over the place.

He should be up-to-date with vaccinations and worming procedures. His feet should be kept well trimmed and every effort made to keep his coat clean and brushed. It may be necessary to trim back long hair from his abdomen and around the genitals before the season starts.

A male that has been reared from a kid will generally be easier to handle, especially if he wears a neck collar and is accustomed to being led. A more difficult one may need a head collar to make control easier.

Artificial insemination

Goatkeepers who live in an area where there is no shortage of stud males usually have no problem about having their goats mated. There are areas where the nearest male goat may be more than a day's journey away, so that it is not feasible to rely on someone else's male. In this case, keeping one's own male may be appropriate even for small-scale operations. Alternatively, artificial insemination could be considered.

With AI, the semen of top quality males can be used, without the need to transport goats or to have the feeding costs of keeping a stud male. You will need to have a fairly accurate knowledge of when the female is likely to come into 'heat', or to be receptive to the sperm. The sperm is sold in 'straws'. One of these is introduced into the vagina of the goat using a special applicator. It is not a practice to be undertaken without proper tuition, and anyone who is interested in artificial insemination is recommended to seek out and enrol in one of the inseminator courses that are available.

Mating
The heat period

The breeding period commences in the autumn. Hormonal action triggers off periods of sexual receptivity on the part of the female. Some goatkeepers use a 'billy rag', one imbued with the scent of the male to encourage coming into heat. Commercial units may insert a sponge impregnated with hormones into the goat's vagina, to induce sexual receptivity and out-of-season breeding, but this is not likely to be of interest to smaller units.

Being in season lasts for anything from a few hours up to three days. It recurs once every 21 days, either until the goat is successfully mated, or the breeding cycle comes to an end in the spring. Signs which indicate being in season are persistent tail-wagging, continuous bleating, a slight discharge from the vulva and general restlessness. Once the tail-wagging and bleating are really in evidence, the goat should be mated as soon as possible. If the male is on site, this is a straight-forward matter of leading her into his exercise yard, making sure that the yard door is securely closed. Then open the door of the house to let him out. If she is really on heat, the male will normally waste no time. It is a good idea to leave them together until a second mating has taken place; this is normally quite soon after the first. It is advisable to have two people to oversee the proceedings, and to control the male.

If it is a question of taking a goat to a male some distance away, it is better to make a provisional booking before the heat period commences. Bear in mind that an official movement form is needed, and a record to and from the site will need to be kept. The stud owner will also wish to see health certification and breed details if a registered breed is involved.

Some studs offer boarding facilities, so that the goat can be taken and left for a couple of days, ensuring that mating will take place at the optimum time. Sometimes taking the goat to a place where she can smell the male is enough to bring her into definite heat. After mating, a certificate to that effect is given.

Pregnancy

If the goat is not in season three weeks later, the chances are that she is pregnant. If you do detect heat symptoms, take her back to the male. If a second mating is also unsuccessful, consult the vet in case there is a problem.

Goats which are born naturally polled (having no horn buds) may also prove to be infertile. It is not always the case, but if you have a naturally polled goat, it is unwise to mate her with a naturally polled male, for this increases the chances of her having infertile kids.

Occasionally a goat shows all the symptoms of pregnancy, including putting on weight. Then the uterus expels fluid, but no kid. This is called 'cloudburst' or false pregnancy. The exact cause is unknown, although it is more common in first-year goats which are being allowed to go into their second year before mating. The same goat usually kids normally the following year.

General management

General management of the pregnant goat is important. She may need worming in the first month and have her feet trimmed before she gets to the heavy stage where damage and stress could result. She should not be expected to go through narrow entrances or be in any stressful situation such as having to cope with noisy dogs. Other measures are to ensure that an anti-clostridial injection is administered a few weeks before kidding. The effect of this is to prevent enterotoxaemia in the mother, and the immunity is passed to the kids via the bloodstream.

When a goat is in-kid for the first time, the concentrate ration should be increased from around the sixth week, to take into account the developing kids. A gradual increase should be aimed for in order to prevent upsets. The approximate quantities are as follows:

A large, dairy goat: 1 - 1.5kg.
Fibre and meat goats: 400 - 500g
Pygmy goats: 200 - 300g.

Drying off

If it is a mature dairy goat which is in-kid, she will need to be dried off at least two months before kidding. Most will do this naturally. Leaving a little milk behind in the udder each time she is milked will mean that less is produced next time. Veterinary dry mammary tubes can also be used at the end to ensure that milk has ceased altogether. While being dried off, the concentrate ration can be reduced slightly, but once the milk has stopped completely and the goat is around six weeks from kidding, the amount should be increased, as indicated above.

Hay should be made available to appetite. As much twiggy growth as possible can be given, but too much lush green foods should be avoided in the drying off period. She should have plenty of exercise in the yard or pasture.

Body condition scoring

A good way of determining how much concentrate a goat needs at any particular time is to check its body condition. Run your hand along the spine and assess the amount of flesh on either side of it. A reasonable covering is what is required. If the spine projects in an emaciated way, more feeding is required. If the spine can hardly be felt, the goat is approaching obesity.

Saanen Milker. *(Peter Cox)*

Toggenburg milker. *(Peter Cox)*

British Saanen Milker. *(Peter Cox)*

A newly kidded British Toggenburg with her kids. *(Katie Thear)*

Anglo Nubian milker. *(Peter Cox)*

Golden Guernsey females. *(Katie Thear)*

British Alpine milker. *(Peter Cox)*

English milker. *(English Goat Breeders' Association)*

Bagot goats. *(Bagot Goat Breed Society)*

Boer male. *(Harry Fuller)*

Angoras. *(Stephen Whiteley)*

Cashmere goats. *(Margaret Merchant, The Macaulay Institute).*

70

Harness goats. *(Katie Thear)*

Goats are natural browsers. *(Katie Thear)*

A trailer with a ramp for easy access is needed for transporting goats. *(ISA-Lloyd Trailers)*

Pygmy goat. *(Katie Thear)*

A line-up of British Alpines at a goat show. *(Katie Thear)*.

Kidding

It is important that no pregnant woman helps at kidding times. Goats can pass on a viral infection which can cause abortion in pregnant women.

Presentation of kid for birth

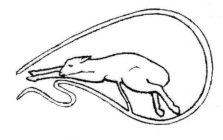

The average gestation period for goats is 5 months (150 days) but kidding is possible at any time from 140 days onwards. If the female is normally communally housed, she should be given her own thoroughly clean pen with clean, fresh straw. Most goats lie down to give birth, but a few prefer to stand.

The udder will become fuller for anything up to several weeks before, so this is not a reliable indication that kidding is imminent. Sometimes the udder becomes so full that it causes discomfort. If she is seen to be frequently kicking her back leg, it is probably the reason. As a general rule, she should not be milked at this stage, but a little milk can be drawn off to ease the discomfort.

A certain indication that kidding will soon take place is the softening of the rump area, when two definite hollows develop, one on each side of the tail. The goat goes off her food and frequently paws at the straw in her pen. From this time, regular checking is advisable. It is not uncommon to find that the kids have arrived without warning. I had a goat that invariably had twins, always managing to have them licked clean and dry before discovery.

Helping at delivery

Once a goat begins to strain, the kids are being pushed down the birth canal. The vulva increases in size and the first sight of the kid will be when the 'water bag' begins to emerge. If this breaks, as it usually does, the two front legs, with a nose resting on top, will be seen. Once the head and shoulders are through, the rest slips out easily and the goat will usually give a loud bellow. If she has been standing up, the umbilical cord will have been stretched sufficiently to break. If lying down, she will break it as she licks the kid.

Without interfering too much, check that the nostrils are free of mucus and that the kid is breathing. Rub it dry with a towel or kitchen roll and place it on some clean straw in a warm corner of the pen from where it is not able to roll away or

73

Young kids keeping warm in a corner of the pen. *(Katie Thear)*

be trampled upon. A large, shallow box is ideal. If the mother can see her kid, she will not object, particularly if she is concentrating on the next birth.

A goat can have any number from one to five kids, although two or three is usual. Once they are all born, the afterbirth will follow, although it could be several hours before it comes away. If it shows no likelihood of doing so, do not attempt to pull it, but consult the veterinary surgeon whose telephone number should be close to hand. A vet's help is also needed if there is obviously a problem in the actual kidding.

A goat which has been straining for more than half an hour to no effect, is in urgent need of assistance. Sometimes the cervix does not dilate properly, a condition known as 'ring womb'. Another potentially serious condition is when the presentation of the kid is such that it is unable to be voided. Sometimes it is simply a matter of pushing the kid back slightly and manipulating it into the correct position with its head resting on the front feet. If it is not possible to achieve this, the vet should be called immediately. It goes without saying that any physical manipulation of this nature requires scrubbed and disinfected hands. The vet will prescribe an antibiotic if there is a risk of womb infection.

Post-natal care

Remove the afterbirth from the pen and put in some clean bedding straw. If the mother is heavily soiled she should be sponged clean and then dried. There will be a pinkish discharge from the vagina for a few days after kidding, but this is normal, unless it develops a foul smell. If it does, or she has a temperature, contact the vet, for it is probably an infection of the womb, requiring an immediate antibiotic.

The mother will appreciate a drink of warm water more than anything else immediately after kidding. This period is crucial. Give no concentrates at all on this or the day after kidding, but plenty of hay. The concentrates should then be introduced and increased gradually. These precautions will help to minimise the possibility of milk fever. (See page 117). It is always preferable to underfeed concentrates at this stage rather than to overfeed.

Once the kids are being bottle-fed, the mother will gradually be brought to full milk production, following the same formula in relation to maintenance and production that was referred to earlier. Hay should be available at all times when she is in her stall or in the goat yard. Grazing will be dependent on weather, with green food and fodder crops as available.

The only other requirement that the mother may need is a worming preparation to ensure that she continues to be free of worms.

The kids

As soon as the kids are born and their breathing has been checked, the umbilical cord can be sprayed with an iodine solution. They should be checked for any defects such as supernumerary (extra) teats, and obvious deformities such as misshapen limbs or defective jaw structures. It is best to have them put down immediately, by a licensed slaughterer or the vet.

It is easy to distinguish between males and females. There is no point in keeping the males unless there is a particularly good reason. Male kids of dairy breeds have little commercial value although they could be reared for the freezer.

It is important that once the kids are licked or rubbed clean, they should suckle as soon as possible. Most will do this as soon as they are with their mother. Sometimes small kids have difficulty in suckling over-large teats. In this case, it is best to milk out a little milk and put it in a sterilised bottle with a rubber teat. It ensures that the kids have the vital colostrum, the first milk which is rich in nutrients and antibodies.

Kids which do not have colostrum are unlikely to survive because they do not receive the natural immunity afforded by the antibodies. If there is a surplus of it, it can be stored in the freezer for later use or for emergencies.

Sometimes a premature birth may occur. If the kids are particularly small, they will be unable to feed themselves. Their needs are warmth and colostrum. The first will be from a heat lamp such as that used for lambs. The second must come from the mother by milking out a little colostrum, unless there is some in the freezer for emergencies. Warm it up and add a little glucose, then dribble a little into the kids' mouths with a dropper. Premature kids may be unable to suck on normal rubber teats and a dropper-type feeder may be needed. Vets can often help with the supply of a suitable feeder.

A combined bottle feeder *(Katie Thear)*   Right: Bottle-feeding an Angora kid *(Katie Thear)*

Feeding a little every hour may just pull them through until they are strong enough to suck. It is possible that the mother will reject them if you try to reintroduce them at this stage. If so, they will need to be bottle-fed until weaned.

Disbudding

Kids should be disbudded at the age of four days if possible, but certainly before they are a week old. This is the process of cauterising the horn buds so that the horns do not grow. The procedure is a simple one, but should only be carried out by a veterinary surgeon.

Earmarking and registration

The law requires that all goats born after 31st December 2009 are ear-tagged ordinarily within six months of birth. (See Page 9). A pure-bred kid can also be registered with the appropriate breed society. Requirements are the certificate of identification of the mother and the mating certificate issued by the owner of the stud male.

Rearing

It is normal for a dairy goat kid to spend the first four days with its mother. In this way, it receives the essential colostrum, the first thick milk which contains antibodies from the dam. While they are with the mother, the kids will take comparatively little milk from her at first, and may go to the same teat each time.

Newly-disbudded kids. *(Dorset Echo)*

This can have the effect of distorting the udder unless care is taken to milk the other teat and balance the amount taken overall. After four days, the kids will be separated from the mother and weaned onto a bottle. Non-dairy goats are normally left with the mother until natural weaning takes place.

The kids are best housed together in a large pen with plenty of straw so that they keep warm, as well as providing company for each other.

Bottle-feeding Kid replacement feeds are widely available. Lemonade bottles are suitable as feeders, and rubber teats made for goat kids will fit them. The teats may be of the plug-in, pull-on or screw-on variety. Where several kids are being reared, individual bottles can be time consuming. An alternative is to use a combined feeder. (See page 75). Feeders must be sterilised before use.

Warm the milk to blood heat. Hold the kid gently, using the thumb to open its mouth slightly and insert the teat, squeezing it slightly to make some of the milk dribble out. It does not usually take long for the kid to associate the bottle with food, and it sucks vigorously as a result. Start with approximately 200ml of milk, four times a day, gradually increasing the amount to meet demand, until around 1.5 - 2 litres a day are taken, depending on the breed. By this time, the number of feeds will have been reduced to three a day. Water to drink, and hay, should be available from the start. The kids will not eat much hay initially, but will play with it and enjoy nibbling. A few concentrates can be given from the second week.

Weaning As it begins to take more hay and concentrates, the process of weaning can begin from between three to five months. By this time about 225g of concentrate per day will be consumed, with hay given on an ad-lib basis. A little green food can be introduced as soon as there is evidence of interest. A mineral lick should be made available.

By the age of five to six months the kid will be completely weaned and taking ad-lib hay with coarse mix concentrates between 250-600g a day, depending on their size and type. Avoid giving too much to goatlings that are not to be mated until their second year.

At weaning time, the kids may need to be wormed if they have been on pasture with the mother. It is also an appropriate time to check their feet in case they need a trim. At about this age they should have their first anti-clostridial injection to protect them against the soil-borne organisms that can cause disease. They should be revaccinated once a year.

Depending on the weather, kids will be able to go out to pasture when they are weaned. Those that are reared by the mothers will normally accompany them outside earlier, particularly if there is a scrambling area in a yard for them. They will derive enormous enjoyment from playing on a group of logs or boulders. It is important that they are not subjected to cold, damp weather and that if they go out to pasture, the grass is fresh and clean.

Training kids

Kids can be trained from an early age. Get them used to wearing a collar. They are available and a small dog lead can be clipped on. Practising walking on the lead is an excellent way of getting a kid used to control. A lot of patience is required, with many words of praise where deserved, but also kind firmness if there is any pulling on the lead. Do not to let them jump up on you! This may be delightful when they are small, but it is a different story when they are older. If they try to jump or push, just walk away. They will soon learn.

Goat's Milk

For many people, the reason for keeping goats is in order to have their own milk supply, but there is a widely-held belief that goat's milk tastes 'goaty'. In fact, if milk is produced hygienically from well-fed dairy goats, and the milk is cooled straight after milking, it should be impossible for most people to distinguish between it and cow's milk. Any dairy animal's output is obviously influenced by what it eats. There are incidences of milk being tainted by certain plants such as cabbage, wild garlic, wild onion and turnips, but these tend to be where an excess is eaten. For example, if a goat is browsing in pasture where wild garlic is plentiful, this may affect the milk. If, despite scrupulous attention to milk hygiene and diet, a particular goat does appear to be producing tainted milk, there are four possibilities to look into:

- When milking, have you been splashing the milk into the bucket? This increases the oxygen content and breaks up the fat particles, factors which are conducive to a more rapid production of fatty acids in the milk.

- Check that there are no active musk glands behind the horn area. These will give a goaty smell around the head. A veterinary surgeon will cauterise them.

- Have the goat's urine tested for a possible high level of ketones. These are by-products of the conversion of stored body fats, a situation which occurs when a goat is under-fed. Immediate treatment is afforded by proper feeding and giving glucose as a short-term expedient.

- Ensure that the goat is not carrying an intolerable worm burden, by giving her a proprietary worming preparation available from the vet.

If all these points have been taken care of but there is still a taint, the culprit is likely to be inadequate milk handling technique. Filter, pasteurise and cool the milk immediately. Then use it as fresh as possible, keeping it in refrigerated conditions in the meantime.

Milking

Milking Stand

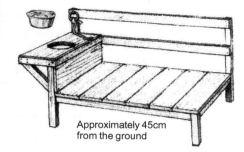

Approximately 45cm
from the ground

Milking Sequence

Position
of hand

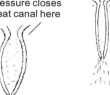

1. Pressure closes
off teat canal here

2. Pressure maintained here

3. Pressure here forces out milk

Pre-milking check

After wiping the teats,
a little milk is squirted into
the black strip cup so that
any clots indicating
mastitis will show up.

Teat Dipping

Each teat dipped in
antiseptic solution
after milking

Treating Mastitis

Section of tube
inserted into
teat canal

Antibiotic
intramammary
tube

Mastitis can be treated with an intramammary
tube of antibiotic. Milk must be discarded
during treatment and withdrawal time.
Homoeopathic remedy is an alternative.

Milk Treatment

Filter the milk with a fine
nylon strainer or with a
purpose-made filter unit

Filter unit with filter discs

Pasteurise by heating to
72°C and cool immediately

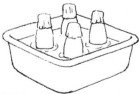

Pour milk into containers, cap and cool in cold
water. Refrigerate at a maximum of 5°C

The udder

A goat's udder is divided into two quarters, each quarter ending in a teat outlet. (See Page 15) 'Two quarters' is a paradox in terms, but it stems from the fact that a cow's udder has four quarters and the terminology has been extended to goats, despite the fact that they have only two teats to the cow's four.

Each quarter is separate from the other and is held in place by suspensory ligaments. Milk constituents are delivered by the blood stream into the secretory tissue of the udder (the alveoli). From here, milk drains into the central udder cistern above the teat. A section of tissue temporarily closes off the udder cistern from the teat canal when the top of the teat is squeezed during milking. Squeezing the lower part of the teat thus propels milk out of the teat opening. Once released, the canal fills up again from the cistern.

Milking

Where goat's milk is being sold, the goats will be machine-milked in a specially adapted milking parlour. Where the milk is for domestic consumption only, they may be hand-milked but the milking area should be quite separate from the sleeping area. This is a question of hygiene, for it is important that the milk should be as free as possible from dust and other contaminants.

On a small, domestic scale, the milking area may even be outside, as long as the weather is dry. I have often milked goats outside in the sunshine, listening to the birds and enjoying the open air. In wet weather a small lean-to area outside the house is satisfactory, although wintery weather calls for more protected conditions.

A goat is considerably smaller than a cow. The udder is closer to the ground and milking can impose a strain on the back of the milker. A milking stand with a stool can alleviate the problem. Around 45cm from the ground is an appropriate height. A stand can be constructed by anyone with a reasonable knowledge of carpentry.

Machine milking

There are basically two types of milking machine system available:

- A portable, self-contained and wheeled unit suitable for one or two goats at a time. This is electric or petrol driven and the milk is pumped into a specialised 'bucket' which filters the milk as it enters.
- For larger numbers, a pipeline system is normally used. This has the individual teat clusters leading into a central pipeline which pumps the milk

into a bulk tank. Here the milk is filtered as it enters, and is immediately cooled to 5°C. Milking units for cows are not suitable for goats because the teat clusters are different in size. The vacuum pressure is also higher on milkers for cows. If used on goats, the teat clusters may be drawn too high, pinching the area above the top of the teat canal, and causing damage to the udder.

Machine milking a commercial herd. *(Fullwood)*   Learning to hand-milk at a farm club. *(Katie Thear)*

Hand milking

The basic procedure is to hold the teats in such a way that the top of the index fingers and thumbs close off the top of the teat canals, while the rest of the hands - the remaining fingers and palms - squeeze the bottom part of the canal. This has the effect of forcing milk out of the teat openings. After the milk has gone, the pressure at the top of the canals is released, allowing them to fill up again from the milk cistern, and the procedure is repeated. It is usual for this to alternate with the two teats, so that a rhythm of milking is established.

On no account should the teats be pulled down. This is the most common error in hand milking. The hands should remain at the same level throughout. Another frequent fault is to pinch off the top of the teat canal too high so that the tissues above are hurt. Any goat, no matter how even-tempered, is likely to react to such treatment, usually by plonking her foot firmly in the milking pail.

Infinite patience is required when milking a goat for the first time. A first kidder may have sore teats and using a purpose-made udder ointment to soothe them is essential. Another aspect to bear in mind is that long nails can hurt a goat. They should be kept short and neatly filed.

Milking routine

Whatever the scale of milking, the following principles are essential, if an acceptable standard of hygienic milk handling is to be maintained, and if contented, unharrassed goats are to be the aim.

Prepare the area Put food in containers to keep the goats contented while being milked. If they are hand-milked, the milking pail should be washed out with hot water and have a lid. Milking machines should be checked to ensure that filters are in place and that the system is operating smoothly.

Prepare yourself Wear an overall kept specifically for milking and keep long hair covered. Wash your hands thoroughly before starting.

Prepare the goats Once on the milking stand and yoked in position, the goat will be tucking into its food. Wipe the udder and teats clean. Proprietary dairy cleansing and sterilising agents are widely available for this purpose. Make sure that the udder is quite dry before milking.

Check the milk Check the first few squirts of milk from each teat for the presence of mastitis This is an infectious condition of the udder which indicates its presence in clots of milk. If you are hand-milking, use a strip cup. This is a purpose-made cup with a black, detachable interior dish. Any clots in the milk will show up against the dark surface. Pipeline units normally have mastitis detectors incorporated within them.

Milk quickly and efficiently The sequence is shown on Page 80 but it is a good idea to have the technique demonstrated by an experienced goatkeeper. With machine milking, the average time is two to three minutes at a speed of around 80—90 pulsations a minute. Hand-milking speed will obviously vary with individuals, but is usually around five minutes to a quarter of an hour. The goat becomes used to a certain time and, if she thinks a new milker is taking longer than necessary, is likely to become fidgety.

Carry out teat dipping This is a simple procedure to ensure that the possibilities of mastitis are kept to a minimum. A teat cup containing an antiseptic preparation is held under the udder and the end of each teat is dipped in it. Once this simple procedure has been carried out, the goats are released and taken back to their yard, pens or pasture, as the case may be.

Clean the milking area and equipment All milking equipment should be rinsed in cold water, then in hot water. Pails are stored upside down until needed next time. Milking machines need special procedures of washing and disinfecting. Follow the manufacturer's instructions.

Buckets may, over a period of time, acquire a layer of 'milk stone', particularly in hard water areas. In itself this is harmless, but it may provide an area where bacteria may become lodged. Dairying suppliers sell a purpose-made product based on phosphoric acid for removing this.

The milking area - floor and milking stand will also need to be cleaned in case any droppings have been deposited there during milking.

Processing the milk

Once you have extracted the milk from the goats, it is time to take it to the milk processing area. Depending on the scale of operations, this will either be the household kitchen or a purpose-built dairy. It is here that the filtering, cooling and, if necessary, the pasteurisation should take place.

Filter the milk The milk needs to be filtered in case any extraneous matter such as the occasional hair has fallen into it. Machine systems will have filter units in the pipeline. Hand milkers will need to do it manually. You can buy small filtering units, which consist of a holder with disposable filter papers to fit, which is placed on top of a stainless steel bucket. You simply pour the milk from the milking pail through the filter. On a very small scale, where the milk is for domestic use only, a fine nylon kitchen strainer will suffice.

Pasteurising Pasteurisation is a heat treatment that was invented by French scientist Louis Pasteur during the nineteenth century. It involves heating the milk and then quickly cooling it prior to bottling. The process kills bacteria making the milk safe to drink. Although some would contend milk is safe as it leaves the udder anyway, pasteurisation will kill most heat-resistant, non-spore-forming, pathogenic bacteria likely to be present in milk. Basically these are Mycobacterium tuberculosis, the cause of TB, and Coxiella burnetti, the cause of Q fever. The process will also prolong the storage life of the milk.

There are two methods, the high temperature, short time method and the low temperature, longer time method. In the high temperature method the milk is raised to 72°C for a period of 15 to 25 seconds and then reduced as quickly as possible to 4°C. In the low temperature method the milk is raised to 63°C and held at that for 30 minutes.

On a small scale either method can be undertaken at home, the only special equipment being required is an accurate thermometer. Digital probe versions being the easiest to use. Put the milk into a large thick bottomed pan and bring to temperature, stirring frequently to avoid the milk scorching on the base of the pan.

The benefit of a probe thermometer is that you can ensure the milk is at temperature throughout the pan. Remember it is likely to be hotter near the heat source at the base and, because heat rises, at the top. Hence the stirring.

With the low temperature method, turn the heat down to just holding and stir occasionally, checking the temperature. Place a lid on the pan to keep the heat in.

Once the milk has been pasteurised, skim off any skin that may have formed on the surface then pour into previously washed and sterilised bottles or other containers. They can then be cooled by placing them in a sink of cold, running water before you remove them to the refrigerator.

The problem of using one saucepan to heat the milk is that it can be difficult to avoid scorching and imparting a burnt flavour to the milk. Using a large jam or preserving pan with a trivet in the base filled with water and then heating the milk in a another pan in the hot water bath avoids this problem.

Purpose made small scale pasteurisers are available but they are not cheap. Large, commercial herds will have a pasteurisation unit as part of the milk handling system.

Packaging and storage On a domestic scale, glass bottles with tops are suitable for storing milk. Cartons and plastic bags are also available if the milk is to be frozen. In a refrigerator, the temperature should not exceed 5°C. When it is stored in a freezer the temperature should stay below - 18°C.

Dairy Products

Good huswife in dairie that needs not be told
Deserveth her fee to be paid hir in golde.
(Thomas Tusser. 16th Century).

Milk can be transformed into a variety of products, including yoghurt, cheese, butter and ice cream. Most goatkeepers use their kitchens as a dairy. If produce is to be sold, a separate dairy site must be registered and inspected according to the requirements of *Milk and Dairying Regulations.*

The book *Cheesemaking and Dairying* is recommended as a comprehensive guide to producing dairy products for home consumption or for sale.

Yoghurt

The micro-organisms responsible for producing yoghurt are *Lactobacillus bulgaricus, L. acidophilus* and *Streptococcus thermophilus.* They are available in pure form as yoghurt 'starters' from dairying suppliers. Alternatively, a little 'live' yoghurt or yoghurt from a previous batch can be used as a starter.

Ingredients: 1 litre goat's milk
1 tablespoon plain live goat's milk yoghurt or bought starter

Method: Heat the milk in a saucepan until it is just about to simmer. This is at 72°C when the heat pasteurises the milk and kills off any unwanted micro-organisms. A dairy thermometer is useful here. Now cool the milk until it reaches 43°C. Pour most of the milk into a thermos flask which has been previously rinsed out with boiling water. Blend the rest of the milk with the live yoghurt and pour it into the flask. Put on the lid and give the flask a good shake, then place it in a warm place, such as an airing cupboard, and leave overnight. The following day, transfer the yoghurt to a bowl, pouring off any thin surface liquid, and leave to firm in the refrigerator. Once cooled, it is ready for eating.

Although good results can be had from using live yoghurt as a starter, it is not always reliable. A surer method is to use a purpose-made starter. These are available from dairying suppliers and from many health food shops. They normally come in small sachets, but occasionally in liquid form, and it is important to follow the manufacturer's instructions.

A range of cheesemaking and dairying equipment for the home. *(Katie Thear)*

A common problem with some goat's milk is that the yoghurt is thin and runny. This is usually because the milk itself is thin and lacking in proteins. Some strains of goats, particularly those which produce large volumes of milk, may not necessarily yield good quality milk with the required level of proteins. The Anglo-Nubian breed, for example, is often the choice over the British Saanen (for yoghurt production) because its milk is thicker. One way of overcoming the problem of thin yoghurt is to add a little powdered milk to the original milk before incubation. Dried goat's milk is available from specialist suppliers.

Butter

To obtain cream for butter making, leave the milk to stand overnight in a wide, shallow saucepan. It should be covered and left in a cool place. The following day, heat it very gently, when more cream will rise to the surface to join that which has already collected overnight. Turn off the heat and skim the cream from the surface with a perforated ladle. Do this with several batches of milk over a period of days until there is enough cream to churn, storing the cream in the refrigerator in the meantime. Anyone with a cream separator is in the position of being able to separate far more of the available cream. It operates by using centrifugal force to separate the cream from the buttermilk.

Small hand-operated butter churns are also available. The most common type has a glass dish with a screwtop lid which incorporates an external handle for turning the internal paddle. After the cream has been churned and the butter particles formed, pour off the liquid buttermilk and leave it to one side for later use. (It can be used for making scones.) Now add cold water to the churn to rinse away the last traces of buttermilk. Empty the butter into a kitchen colander lined with butter muslin or close-weave netting which has been previously boiled, and squeeze out the rest of the liquid. Sprinkle on a little salt to taste. Form the butter into a pat and place in a dish. Store in the refrigerator.

Cheese

Soft cheeses are quick and relatively easy to make, and require little in the way of equipment. Pressed cheeses need more equipment, including a proper cheese press, and are more complicated and time-consuming to make. Sterilise all the equipment in hot water before starting.

Soft goat's cheese

Ingredients: 2 litres fresh, full cream goat's milk
2 tablespoons live yoghurt or live buttermilk *
2 drops rennet

Method: Pasteurise the milk then cool to 22°C and add the starter. Dilute the rennet in a little previously boiled and cooled water and stir in. Cover and leave in a warm place (21-22°C) overnight. The following day, ladle the curds into a previously boiled cheesecloth, make into a bundle and hang to drain for 24 hours. Remove from the cloth and add salt and black pepper to taste. It is now ready to eat but will keep in the refrigerator for around three days.

Pressed goat's cheese

This takes longer to make and requires a longer ripening period before it is ready to eat. It is paler yellow than Cheddar cheese but has a similar taste. This recipe makes approximately 500g of cheese.

Ingredients: 5 litres full cream milk
1 litre additional cream (optional)
Half a cup of live yoghurt or live buttermilk*
3ml (half teaspoon) rennet   10g salt

Method: Pasteurise the milk and cool to 22°C. Stir in the starter and leave the milk, covered in a warm place for about an hour so that it can acidify.

Increase the temperature to 28°C. Mix the rennet with two teaspoonfuls of previously boiled and cooled water and then stir it in. Cover the container and then leave the milk to set in a warm place. The curd is normally ready when it is firm to the touch, gives slightly and does not leave a milk stain on the back of the finger. Note that with vegetarian rennet, setting takes longer than with animal rennet. It also takes longer in a cooler environment.

Cut down into the curd, from top to bottom one way then cut it at right angles to form square columns. Now cut horizontally to form pieces. The curd is then loosened from around the walls of the pan. Stir gently with the hand for a couple of minutes.

Gradually increase the temperature to 38°C, while occasionally stirring, over the next 30-40 minutes. Give a final, circular stir so that it whirls round. The curds then gradually sink to the bottom and collect at a central point. Turn off the heat and leave the pan until all movement has ceased in the liquid.

Ladle out as much of the liquid whey as possible, then place a previously sterilised cloth over a stainless steel bucket or large basin and tip in the curds. Make the cloth into a bundle by winding one corner around the other three. Place the bundle on a tray which is tilted at an angle to let the whey drain away. Leave for about 15 minutes. Untie the bundle and the curds will be seen to have formed into a mass. Cut this into four slices and place one on top of the other then cover with the cloth. After 15 minutes place the outer slices of the curd on the inside of the stack, and vice versa. Repeat several times until the curd resembles the texture of cooked breast of chicken when it is broken open.

Break up the curd into pea-sized pieces and sprinkle on 10g salt. Line the cheese mould from the cheese press with previously boiled cheesecloth and add the curd until the mould is full. The corner of the cloth is then folded over the top of the cheese and it is ready for pressing. Once in the mould the wooden 'follower' is placed on

---

* Best results are obtained by using a commercial starter. Follow their instructions because they vary, depending on the manufacturer.)

top so that when the mould is put into the press there is a surface on which to exert an even pressure. For the first hour, apply a light pressure so that the fats are not lost with the whey, then increase it to the maximum and leave until the following day.

Next day, remove the cheese from the press, replace the cloth with a clean one and put the cheese back in the mould, upside down, and press for another 24 hours. Remove the cheese from the press and cloth and dip it in hot water (66°C) for one minute in order to consolidate and smooth the surface. Place it in a protected area at a temperature of 18-21°C and leave it to dry for a day or two until a rind begins to form.

Once the rind has formed the cheese can be sealed to prevent it becoming unduly dry while maturing. Large cheeses are often bandaged but it is easier to use cheese wax that is available from specialist suppliers. Leave to mature in a cool, dry place at 8 − 11°C. Turn it regularly. It should be ready after a month.

Ice cream

Small quantities of ice cream can be made at home with the minimum of equipment. Domestic ice cream makers are available, but all that is necessary is a food mixer, a shallow dish and the freezing compartment of a refrigerator (or a deep freeze). The following recipe is easy to make and is popular with adults as well as children.

Ingredients:	500ml milk	1 small carton double cream
	2 level tablespoons sugar	1 level tablespoon cornflour
	1 beaten egg	4 drops vanilla essence

Method: Mix the cornflour with a little of the milk in a bowl, making sure that there are no lumps. beat the egg until light and fluffy and add to the cornflour. Stir in the sugar, add the vanilla essence and then pour in the rest of the milk.

Stir the mixture well and place in a bowl over a water bath or on top of a saucepan of water and heat, stirring all the time. The mixture is ready when it has thickened to a custard. Allow the mixture to cool. Whisk the cream until it stands in peaks then blend into the cold mixture. Put into a shallow container and freeze until slushy, then remove and stir well. This is to incorporate any cream on the surface and to prevent large ice crystals forming. Return to the freezer until frozen. Before use, place in an ordinary refrigerator to soften.

If any dairy products are sold, the site must be registered and meet all the regulatory requirements. (See page 125). Insurance cover is also advisable.

Goats for Meat

I killed a she-goat and her kid followed me home.
(Robinson Crusoe. Daniel Defore)

Kids reared for meat are often surplus males, but the Boer goat is specifically a meat breed. Some goatkeepers, who only require their milking goats to be in milk, therefore cross them with a Boer male so that the kids are more suitable for raising as meat animals.

After four days with the mother in order to have colostrum and a good start, the kids are switched to a communal pen. There is no need to separate the sexes at this stage. The males will not normally show sexual behaviour until the age of three months, but watch out for precocious ones and separate if necessary. They can be reared until 8 - 10 weeks and then slaughtered.

The kids' communal pen will need a thick layer of straw for bedding, and it should be well protected from draughts. If it has gaps in the walls, rather than solid board partitions, it is a good idea to place straw bales around it as insulation. Unless it is cold, they are unlikely to need a heat lamp, for they will snuggle up to each other to keep warm.

A milk replacer can be given in place of the mother's milk after four days. At first, give around 200ml of milk, four times a day, gradually increasing the amount to meet demand, until around 1.5 - 2 litres a day are taken. By this time, the number of feeds will have been reduced to three a day. Water to drink should be introduced right from the start.

A concentrate ration can be introduced in the second week. Once they get to the age of six weeks, the concentrate ration can be boosted. A barley based ration is a suitable one and a possible mixture is: 2 parts barley flakes: 1 part soya bean meal: 1 part flaked maize. Alternatively an ordinary coarse goat ration can be given. Hay should be available, at all times.

Around 8 - 10 weeks is an appropriate time to have them slaughtered and this can be done at a local abattoir, with the meat being jointed and returned in bags ready for the freezer. A trailer that is equipped for the safe transport of the goats will be needed and a date should be booked in advance with the abattoir. If you want to have the skin back for curing, let them know. They may add a little extra to the charge for this.

Boer x kids. *(Katie Thear)*

Greek-style goat

Ingredients:
One leg of kid meat
1 teaspoon dried oregano
Juice of half a lemon

1 garlic clove
4 tablespoons olive oil
Salt and black pepper to taste

Method: Place the leg in a baking tin and rub it with the crushed garlic. Sprinkle on the salt, pepper and oregano. Mix together the olive oil and lemon juice and pour over the joint.

Roast in a medium oven, removing after half an hour to baste the joint with the liquid. Cook until tender and browned. Serve with new potatoes and peas cooked with a sprig of mint in them.

Goat sausages

Ingredients:
1 kg goat meat
2 level teaspoons salt
12 fresh sage leaves
Sausage casings

10g suet
10g breadcrumbs
Black pepper to taste

92

Sausage casings and sausage-making equipment such as stuffers, mincers, etc, are available from specialist suppliers. (See *Reference Section*).

Mince the meat thoroughly and add the suet. Chop the fresh sage leaves and sprinkle into the mixture with the salt and pepper. Stir in the breadcrumbs and mix well. Stuff the casings with the mixture. Alternatively, sausages without casings can be made by adding a beaten egg to the mixture and then shaping it into sausage shapes with well-floured hands.

Curing a goat skin

The best finish to the skin is obtained by having it cured professionally, but it can be done at home by scraping the fat off the skin then immersing it in a bucket containing 5 litres of hot water into which 400g of alum and 150g of salt are dissolved. Leave to soak for two days then wash well and peg out to dry. As it dries, sprinkle on paraffin and rub with a sandpaper block. Work it thoroughly until it is supple and trim off any unsightly areas around the edges.

Fibre Goats

As with sheep, fibre goats are kept for the crop on their backs. The most common breed is the Angora goat, which produces a fibre called *mohair.* This should not be confused with *angora wool* which comes from rabbits.

There is also *cashmere* fibre, which is very fine and can be realised from any breed that produces a substantial undercoat.

Cashmere goats browsing on pasture. *(Margaret Merchant. The Macaulay Institute).*

Cashgora is a fibre produced through crossing Angora males with any other breed of goat but particularly those with some level of cashmere. Cashgora fibre may be regarded as a half way stage between the two other fibres but this is a over-simplification.

If buying a fibre goat, ask for an up-to-date fleece evaluation document.

Angora goats

There are currently more than 4,000 Angora goats in the UK producing around 25 tonnes of mohair a year. About 10 tonnes of this is used by the producers to turn into mohair products like scarves or shawls for added value, or sold to home spinners. An Angora kid will produce 3-4kg of mohair in its first year and 6-8kg per year after that, although fibre quality gradually deteriorates with age. A good example of the breed will have a generous growth of mohair on the head and neck.

Angoras are normally shorn twice a year in the spring and autumn. They are white in colour, although there are some coloured animals whose fibre is normally popular with home spinners. The coat has some coarse fibres known as *kemp.* Most of this is shed by the kid at around 3-4 months old. The mass of the coat is then made up of long, soft and strong lustrous mohair fibres. The lustre comes from the large cuticle scales on the fibres. Mohair is often called the 'diamond' fibre for this reason.

As well as possessing this sheen, mohair is soft and resilient. It is resistant to creasing and since the fibres are long they are easily processed and blended

A male Angora goat at an agricultural show. *(Katie Thear)*

with other fibres. The first fleece sheared at 6 months old is the finest at around 20 microns in width. As the goat becomes older so the fleece becomes less fine extending up to 40 microns in some older animals.

Husbandry for fibre goats bears some similarity to that for sheep, although the Angora goat has nutritional requirements like those of dairy animals. As with sheep the kids are encouraged to run with their mothers, usually suckling for 4-5 months. During the spring and summer much of the nutritional requirements for Angoras can be met from the pasture, and concentrates may not be necessary, but this depends on the individual needs of each goat. Concentrates should be about 16-18% protein.

The gestation period is usually about 150 days with around 50% of the females producing twins. In early pregnancy, concentrates would be around 200gm per day with ad-lib hay. Within two months of kidding she will need ad-lib hay and around 300gm of concentrates per day. Around kidding the concentrates will have increased to 400gm per day. In early lactation when spring pasture is available, she would receive around 250gm of concentrates per day, increasing to 400gm per day in the latter stages of lactation. Angoras do not fare well in winter conditions in the UK and as with all goats, will need housing. Winter quarters should allow 1.5 - 2.0 sq.m per goat with plenty of ventilation and no draughts. In summer, they need access to rain shelters.

Angora goats need good quality pasture and can be kept at similar stocking rates as sheep with 10 females and followers per hectare. They will need regular foot trimming. A good male can manage around 25 females and would normally be introduced to the flock between August and November.

Cashmere goats

All goats, with the exception of Angoras, produce cashmere in varying quantities. The Cashmere goat is not a breed as such, but one that produces substantial amounts of cashmere fibre. This fibre comes from the downy undercoat grown as a protection against winter weather beneath the guard hairs of the primary top coat. A Cashmere goat is one which has a particularly thick secondary coat, as most feral goats do. Primary fibres are long, coarse and hollow (medullated) forming the greater part of the coat. Both primary and secondary hairs are produced from follicles in the skin. If the secondary hairs are less than 19 microns in diameter they are known as cashmere.

Cashmere is the finest and lightest fibre produced by goats. The spun and woven fabric is warm, light and remarkably tough. It is the most exclusive and expensive of the natural fibres and is used in knitwear, underwear, coats, sportswear, suits, rugs, scarves and even carpets where it imparts softness.

The world's major processing company for cashmere is *Dawson's International* of Selkirk in Scotland. As it buys in large bundles, small producers sell through a cooperative – *The Scottish Cashmere Producers' Association*.

Selective breeding in Scotland which has the appropriate weather conditions, has produced goats with annual yields of 200-300g, with the best animals producing up to 600g. Imported Cashmeres have been crossed with feral goats and there is evidence that they are now breeding true.

Average fibre diameter should be 15 microns. The finer it is, the higher the value. There are three grades. White cashmere has the highest value, followed by grey or brown. Reject fibre is that which is either outside the parameters of cashmere for fineness or does not have the right characteristics of cashmere. This reject fibre is known as Caprine Fine Fibre (CFF).

Cashgora kid, bred from an Angora buck and a dairy goat crossing. *(Ann Attfield)*

Following the grading, the fibre is scoured (washed) to remove all contaminants, dried and then de-haired to separate the top coat (guard hair) from the cashmere. This can be as high as 20%.

Cashmere growth is triggered by the shortening daylight hours although there may also be other factors such as temperature and diet. The coat grows until the end of the year in preparation for the coldest weather. It is then removed in the spring by shearing. If this was not done, the undercoat would gradually loosen and would be shed. It is possible to comb the cashmere from the goat once the undercoat has begun to loosen but this cannot be done at one time and needs two to three occasions to complete. In the meantime, there will be a loss from natural shedding. Combing is not practical or economical.

Shearing

Angora goats are shorn twice a year: in late winter/early spring, before kidding (no later than six weeks before kidding), and again in the autumn, before mating. Cashmere goats are shorn once, in late winter to early spring, before kidding. After shearing, the Cashmere goats need to kept indoors for several weeks before being allowed out. Shearing in late March produces the maximum yield of cashmere before the coat begins to loosen and fall out.

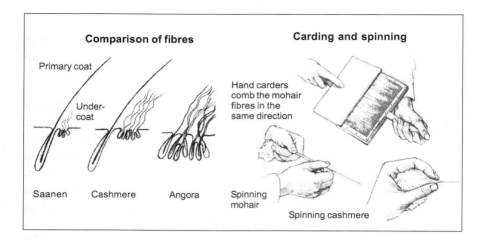

Comparison of fibres

Primary coat

Under-coat

Saanen   Cashmere   Angora

Carding and spinning

Hand carders comb the mohair fibres in the same direction

Spinning mohair

Spinning cashmere

Shearing is the same as for sheep. The goats are rounded up and yarded, and a clean, protected area is set aside for the shearing to take place. White fleeces should be done first, with coloured ones later, to avoid getting coloured fibres in the white.

Shearing is best done in groups with the fleeces from kids, goatlings, does, and bucks kept separate to aid classification. Shearing should obviously not take place in wet weather or when the goats are wet, and a safety circuit breaker should be used, in case of accidents and possible electrocution.

Special goat shearing combs are available for the shearers. Mohair lacks the natural lanolin of sheep's wool and as a result the shears must be used at a slower rate to avoid over-heating.

A pet British Alpine.
It is important to wash hands after handling any animal. *(Katie Thear)*

Spinning

Some goatkeepers keep a small number of fibre goats purely because they provide some very interesting spinning and weaving. The first time I tried to spin pure mohair was with an Australian fleece. It was lustrous and beautiful, but immensely difficult to spin because of the lack of lanolin.

I tried rubbing oil on my hands from time to time, but this was not satisfactory. I eventually settled for mixing it with a little sheep's wool. Such an action is no doubt heresy to mohair producers, but every spinner will sympathise with the problem.

It is possible to spin mohair, of course, but I am not one of the skilled elite of expert spinners, with the dexterity and patience required for fine, luxury fibres. However, what I did glean from my experience of spinning mohair may interest other spinners. I had to decrease the tension on the wheel because it was set for sheep's wool, which is coarser, before the fibres ran smoothly. Because they are so fine, it is easy to overspin, by twisting too much. It requires far less twist to it than the average sheep's wool.

I have no experience of spinning cashmere but a spinning friend tells me that it needs no carding. (Carding is the process of 'combing' fibres to make them lie in the same direction, and make them easier to spin). Tension on the wheel should be loose, and there is no need to feed in the fibres as one would with wool. All that is necessary is to hold it loosely in one hand, letting the wheel draw the fibres.

Home spinners are interested in all fibres. Most would be unlikely to object to mohair with kemp in it, for it is much easier to spin.

Pygmy and Pet Goats

Thy hair is as a flock of goats.
(Song of Solomon)

Most goats are kept as family milk providers. They are usually regarded as pets, particularly if the numbers are small. But what about people who wish to keep goats purely as pets, and who are not necessarily interested in milk production or some other utility characteristic? Does the goat make a suitable pet? The answer is yes, as long as certain basic considerations are met.

Perhaps the most important factor is to choose those that suit the available conditions. If space is limited, it is foolish to have a large breed; a dwarf breed would be more appropriate. Where there are young children, it would be irresponsible to have a strong wilful male goat of one of the large breeds, even if it is a castrated one. Similarly, keeping a goat with horns is also inadvisable. I am aware that some people keep horned Pygmy goats because they feel that the horns are an integral part of the overall appearance. Nevertheless, they are potentially dangerous and young children should avoid horned goats.

Remember that even pet goats need to be registered and earmarked for identification, and at least two will be needed as company for each other. Whichever breed or type is chosen, it is important to remember that the scale of goat-keeping does not affect the quality of management. It is just as important to have a pet goat vaccinated against the range of clostridial diseases as the commercial goat. Similarly, the considerations of ruminant feeding which require a balance of concentrate feeds and roughage are just as vital. Finally, the owner of pet goats has the same legal requirement as the herd owner, to keep a record of all movements of animals on and off the property.

Any breed of goat can be reared as a pet, but the Pygmy goat is the choice of many. Its small size makes

Pygmy goat. *(Katie Thear)*

Inside a shed adapted as a Pygmy goat house. *(Katie Thear)*

it easy to handle and it can be kept in a relatively confined space. It is cheap to feed, with one bale of hay lasting for about a month. It is an attractive little goat, normally found in shades of brown and black, but also with a lighter fawn colouration.

Many owners of Pygmy goats enter them in shows and it is a good idea to visit such a show to see them and to talk to the breeders.

Many pet goats are not milked. Females will come into heat periodically during the breeding season, but if they are kept unmated, they will not produce kids and a flood of milk. Some females may produce milk without kidding. Such 'maiden milkers' will need to be milked to ease the pressure on the udder, but if a little milk is left behind each time, the amount will gradually diminish until she is 'dried off'. The Pygmy produces comparatively little milk even when it has kidded (around 150ml).

Pet goats are simple to house. A shed with an attached concrete run for exercise will cater for two animals. The type of housing sold for larger dogs is ideal for Pygmy goats. The exercise run will need paving slabs or blocks so that the goats are able to climb up and down, and leap about.

Training

It is never too early to start training and it is best to begin when the kids are young. Get them used to wearing collars straight away and clip on a dog lead when taking them for a walk. The principles of training are exactly the same as those used for training a dog. The goat should learn to 'whoah', 'stay' and 'walk on' according to instruction. It should follow you, rather than dragging you along behind it. Remember that you are the herd leader. As with any form of teaching,

Small house and run for Pygmy goats. *(Derek White)*

firm and gentle persuasion is effective. A goat does not respond to punishment and will only be frightened by being smacked. Such treatment is likely to produce the opposite of that intended. Patience, by comparison, is invariably rewarded. A little bribery in the form of titbits will provide pleasant associations and make the learning process easier.

Grooming

All goats need regular care to keep them clean and healthy. The coat will require regular brushing and checking for the presence of parasites such as lice, mites and ticks. Where these are detected, a dusting of a proprietary louse powder or a pour-on from the vet should be applied.

The two areas which require particular attention are the coat and the feet. The coat should be brushed fairly regularly to remove any flaking skin and to promote an active blood circulation to the skin surface. Any matted areas of hair will be removed and the general condition of the coat will show a noticeable improvement with regular brushing. It is a good idea to have two brushes, one fairly stiff and

A Goat Coat

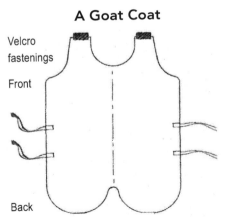

Velcro fastenings

Front

Back

coarse to remove tangles, and a fine soft one to impart a sheen to the coat. The feet need regular trimming to keep the nails from curling around the sole. Details of the foot trimming are given on page 110.

Giving a goat a bath is not difficult, but it should take place only when weather conditions are appropriate. A tin bath which the animal can step into is ideal. A Pygmy goat can be bathed in a plastic baby bath. Ensure that the water is warm without being too hot and encourage the goat to step into it. If it is used to the procedure there should be no difficulty. For this reason, it is wise to accustom kids to being bathed from an early age. A mild shampoo can be used. Avoid using detergents, for these remove the natural oils from the hair and may cause allergic reactions.

Swab the animal all over with a sponge dipped in the soapy water until it is quite clean, then rinse away the suds with clean, warm water. Rub the goat down well with a large towel and brush the hair. On a warm day drying will take place rapidly. After a bath, or in cold periods, the wearing of a coat or rug is advisable. They are available from suppliers, but are not too difficult to make.

Harness Goats

A prudent man does not make the goat his gardener.
(Hungarian Proverb)

Using goats in harness is an old practice known to have taken place in most of the civilisations of the ancient world. At Pompeii, for example, Cupid is depicted driving Bacchus in a cart that is pulled by goats.

Goats have also been used as pack animals, and indeed still are in many parts of the world.

Harness goats in the past have performed various tasks, including acting as water carriers, carting hay and straw, carrying logs, and even delivering the mail and local milk supplies in the last century. They were also popular for giving rides at the seaside in the same period, although they were often badly treated.

The Harness Goat Society, which was formed in 1987, encourages the use of working goats and also makes sure that there is no cruelty involved. Goats in harness are sometimes to be seen at agricultural shows, often forming a cart procession, with their drivers in fancy dress.

Training to harness

Any goat, of either sex, can be trained to harness, but the best choice is a castrated male without horns. Both castration and disbudding should only be carried out by a vet. A hornless, male castrate will be strong and sturdy, without posing a danger, but obviously the earlier that training to harness begins, the more experienced and used to the task he will be.

Young goats are sometimes used to pull small, children's carts, as the photograph opposite illustrates. The important thing is that the cart is in proportion to the goat's capabilities, without imposing the strain of undue weight.

A goat that is to be trained to harness should be accustomed to walking with a collar and lead initially. (See page 102). This can start while it is still a kid so that it becomes accustomed to the instructions 'whoah', 'stay' and 'walk on'. The neck collar can then be replaced with a head collar. Unlike

A disbudded and castrated male trained to pull a cart. *(Katie Thear)*

104

A fancy dress procession of harness goats at an agricultural show. *(Katie Thear)*

a horse's bridle, this does not have a bit in the mouth, but has a sliding chinstrap instead which controls the direction of the head turn.

When the goat is well accustomed to the bridle, and to the instructions that go with it, the rest of the harness can be introduced. This includes a breast collar, traces, breeching (to stop the cart going forward when the goat stops) and saddle or tugs in which the cart shafts are held.

Only when the goat is used to walking about with the harness should the cart be introduced. At first, the time spent pulling the cart should be for short periods only, with much praise given for good behaviour. The pulling times can then be increased gradually as he becomes more experienced. With patience and practice, the goat will be a pleasure to work with.

Goat harnesses are available from specialist suppliers, and it is important to buy those that are appropriate for goats, rather than ones that may have been adapted from horse saddlery.

There is little, it seems, that goats cannot do, although one of the most unusual activities I have come across, is the lady who takes her goat carol-singing before Christmas. The goat, with some decorative glitter around her collar, accompanies the carol singers around the village and they raise money for charity. No one can resist her, but she is apparently not the most tuneful of the carol singers!

Showing Goats

If you put a silk dress on a goat she is still a goat.
(Irish Proverb)

Many people obtain a great deal of pleasure from entering their goats at shows and competitions. This in itself is a good enough reason for having shows, but there are other sound reasons. At a basic level, it brings together goatkeepers of varying experience who can learn from each other. Seeing other people's goats, their plus points and shortcomings, is often a useful guideline in what to aim for in the future. On a wider perspective, shows are about setting and maintaining standards. Over the years, bodies such as the British Goat Society have sought to establish and raise the standards for goats and goatkeeping, and breeders have worked to produce better stock.

There are different types and levels of goat show. The BGS lists all shows which conform to their regulations, and which they recognise. There are also young stock shows run by local goat clubs, often with a section for children.

Preparations for the show

The BGS, like other national goat organisations, publishes a show schedule for the coming year. With a copy of this, select the shows you wish to attend and send off for the required entry details in good time. There are different classes for different goats and it is sometimes quite a lengthy task sorting out the right classes for your particular goats.

Shows vary in size. In large ones the breeds are always separated. In a small club show, there may simply be classes for milkers, goatlings and kids. Whatever the size of the show, there are quite a few preparations.

The goat needs to be a good example of her breed and type and it is here that the importance of studying the breed standards is apparent. There should be no disqualifying faults such as mouth or teat defects.

Only healthy goats should be entered and they need to have CAE certification. (See page 114).

A goat that is be be shown also needs to be able to walk well with her owner, to stand still when required, and to be used to having her mouth inspected. Judges will often lift one of the goat's hind legs in order to examine the udder, and to run their hands over the coat. Being used to these procedures is necessary. These things require periods of training and experience, but a few trial runs before the show will jog her memory, particularly if there is a juicy titbit at the end of each session. Gentle and firm encouragement may produce results, but downright blackmail works wonders.

It is essential that the goat stands well for inspection. *(Katie Thear)*

A few days before the show, trim her hooves. If they are not too long, a few passes of a Surform plane will suffice. It is important for a show goat to be able to walk well, so the finish on her hooves needs to be smooth and even.

The day before the event, trim any untidy hairs from her beard and legs, then give her a shampoo. Many goatkeepers use a dog shampoo, and I have used a baby shampoo to good effect, the principle being that if it does not sting a baby's eyes, it is unlikely to be objectionable to a goat. Purpose-made goat shampoos are also available.

Dry her as quickly as possible, ideally by walking her in the sun. To prevent chilling, she should have a coat or rug put over her. There are also purpose-made goat coats available. A little hoof oil or vaseline helps to bring a shine to the hooves.

There are preparations to be made for the exhibitor as well. A clean white overall for the line-up gives a professional impression, while wellingtons are essential in case it is muddy on the showground.

Pens for the goats are normally provided but you need to take a hay rack, some hay, a drinker, pails, concentrates, and a collar and lead. Where kids are concerned, it may be necessary to take bottles and milk replacer for them.

There are also milking trials at the larger, county shows, but these are for the more experienced. Those with commercial dairy goats often take part in them for they help in identifying and promoting good milking strains.

Those taking part in milking trials need to go to the show the previous evening. This is so that the stewards can strip out milk from the goats. In this way, they all start from an equal position.

The following morning, the goats with their full udders are inspected, then milking takes place. All the pails are taken to be weighed, after which butterfat samples are taken.

Fibre goats are also shown, with the breed standards and health aspects being taken into consideration, as with other goats. The quality of their fibre is obviously an important consideration. In fact, Angora goats are judged 50% on conformation and 50% on the standard of the fleece. Therefore to stand any chance in a show the style and character of the fleece should be up to a recognised standard. There should be no kemp in the fleece.

Fibre goats can be washed but not within a month of the show. Just before the show clean the horns, trim the feet and clean up the tail area.

Health

Prevention is better than cure.

There are certain regular tasks to be undertaken. They include foot trimming, vaccinating and worming. Apart from these the needs of goats are simple; dry housing, fresh air, clean land, a balanced diet of roughage and concentrates, clean fresh water, common sense and affection. A regard for these will keep goats healthy, with few problems. However, it pays to be prepared.

Having somewhere to put a goat if she is off-colour is a good idea. She has peace and quiet in which to recover and convalesce. In the event of there being an infectious condition, the other goats are protected. The pen should be in the quietest part of the house, away from the hub of activity, but where she can still see the other goats at a distance. Goats are gregarious and are distressed if they are on their own.

Sheep hurdles are excellent for making a temporary hospital pen. They slot together quickly and easily, although the gaps in the walls are draughty. The best solution here is to place straw bales outside the pen to provide warm, well insulated walls. If the pen is equipped with a heat lamp, it can be used for all sorts of emergencies such as kiddings.

Being prepared for all eventualities includes having a first aid kit to hand.

Digital rectal thermometer	Hoof paring clippers
Scissors	Surform plane
Sterile cotton wool	Iodine spray
Sterile bandages	Glucose
Antiseptic cream	Kaolin solution
Disinfectant	Cooking oil
Plastic drenching bottle	Udder cream
Tweezers	Tin of molasses or treacle
Hydrogen peroxide	Vaseline

In addition to these basic commodities will be worming preparations and other veterinary prescriptions which will come from the vet as needed.

When it comes to diagnosis of animal ailments, the vet is the only one who can be definite. Symptoms can vary widely from one goat to another, and different conditions may have confusingly similar characteristics. The golden rule is that

Foot trimming is necessary every 6 -8 weeks. *(Katie Thear)*

if there is any doubt, call the vet. The telephone number should be pinned up in a prominent place. It is helpful to be able to give a clear description of the symptoms as you see them, as well as to know the following:

Normal temperature (taken in rectum): 39-39.5°C.
Average pulse rate: 65-95 beats per minute.   *Breathing rate:* 10-30 per minute.
Rumen movement: 1-1.5 per minute.   *Normal dung:* dry and pelleted

Zoonoses: Some conditions can be transferred from goats to humans. Always wash hands after handling them, and ensure that children do so. Pregnant women should avoid helping at kidding. Transferable conditions include: E-coli, cryptosporidia, orf, salmonella and ringworm.

Foot trimming

Goat's feet need regular trimming, every 6-8 weeks. Tie the goat by the collar, or yoke her to a stand, so that she is not able to move too far in any direction. Giving her some tit-bits in a bucket, or an armful of greens, is an excellent way of keeping her occupied.

Hoof paring clippers and a Surform plane are the best tools for the job. The clippers do the main paring, while the plane smoothes it off. (Some prefer to finish off with a sharp knife). Lift the first foot gently, but with a firm hold, and bend the leg in its natural position backwards, without taking it too far back to

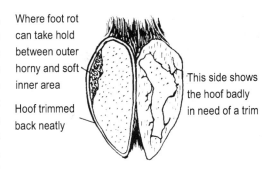

Where foot rot can take hold between outer horny and soft inner area

Hoof trimmed back neatly

This side shows the hoof badly in need of a trim

cause discomfort to the goat. She will probably try to kick her foot free, but if you keep a firm grip and reassure her gently, she will eventually desist.

The trimming is to cut back sections of nail which have grown and possibly curled under the sole. Pare these back carefully, doing a little at a time so as not to cut into the sensitive areas. Clear out any soil or gravel lodged in the hoof, and check for any signs of infection. (See page 116). Use the plane to smooth off.

Worming

Goats out on pasture are at risk from internal parasitic worms. The best way to limit infestation is to control the access to pasture. Eggs deposited during winter browsing will have died off by June. Delaying access to the pasture until July will provide worm larvae-free conditions. Also, a hay crop can be taken beforehand. Grazing kids and goats in spring should be on pasture not grazed during the second half of the previous year by goats or sheep. If grazing during spring, worm goats at kidding time and again in June before moving them onto safe pasture. After worming milking goats, delay using the milk for seven days. If using Oramec delay for 14 days.

The most common parasitic worms are roundworms which infest the gut. They lay eggs which are shed in the droppings and contaminate the herbage. If goats eat the contaminated herbage they take in worm larvae, and so the cycle starts again. Sources of danger of roundworm infection are: pasture where goats or sheep have grazed within the past year, paddocks or areas of strip grazing which are used in rotation, and herbage from pasture spread with goat manure. Safe sources of browse are: newly sown pastures, pasture grazed by cattle or horses, but not goats or sheep, land where hay has just been cut, and browse material such as hay, fodder crops and cut branches

Goats tolerate a certain level of roundworm burden, and develop some immunity. Kids and goatlings are at the most risk, as well as stall-fed goats that suddenly go out to pasture. They have no immunity and will suffer more than those that have acquired resistance over a period of time. Symptoms of infestation are loss of weight, reduced milk, a harsh, staring coat and diarrhoea.

Other types of worm include lungworms that affect the lungs and air passages, causing frequent coughing and a more rapid breathing rate. The intermediate stage of this parasite is carried by snails and slugs so it is more prevalent in wet pastures. Liver fluke occurs in the same conditions. The best way of avoiding both these pests is to keep goats off wet pasture. If necessary it can be drained. DEFRA issues a 'fluke forecast' for the benefit of sheep farmers in Britain. If the forecast is for more flukes than normal for a particular period, it is best to heed it and keep goats off the pasture.

Tapeworms that are carried by dogs can also affect goats. Although these are unlikely to have a serious effect, it is in everyone's interests to keep dogs away from pasture and browsing areas.

Because of the problem of wormer resistance, avoid dosing regularly, unless the goats really do need worming. There are three groups of wormers available. Rotate them each year to minimise resistance. If in any doubt, consult the vet who may take a 'worm count' from a dropping in order to assess the situation and prescribe accordingly. A wormer, given as a liquid drench is administered from a plastic bottle with a curved tube. This is inserted in the side of the goat's mouth, in the gap between the front and back teeth. The key to success is to hold her securely and tip her head back slightly.

Vaccination

Every goat should be vaccinated once a year against the range of clostridial diseases which include enterotoxaemia and tetanus. The procedure is a simple one and well worth it. The vet will advise you and demonstrate how the injection is to be given.

Ailments A-Z

Abortion: There are many reasons why a goat should abort, from accident and stress to deficiency disease and infection. Call the vet without delay.

Abscess: A bacterial infection forming pus under the skin and usually the result of an infected wound. Once it has burst it can be cleaned out and antiseptic applied. If it does not come to head, it may be a cyst. Consult the vet.

Acetonaemia (Ketosis): Essentially a chronic shortage of carbohydrates in the diet. The goat may be pregnant with large kids or a heavy milk yielder not being fed enough to cater for her needs. Ketones are formed in the blood and there is a smell of acetone or nail varnish on the breath. Milk yield declines and there may be off-taints in the milk. Put a little molasses or black treacle in the drinking water and warm it up to make it more attractive. As a fast-acting treatment give a glucose and warm water drench. As soon as she begins to show more interest in food, increase her concentrate cereal ration, giving little and often, and provide good quality hay. The vet should be called, particularly with a pregnant goat.

Anthrax: This is extremely rare in Britain, thanks to the strict regulation which requires that any sudden, unexplained death of livestock is reported. There is no treatment and death is rapid.

Bleating: Continuous bleating can be expected on the following occasions: when the female is on heat; when she has been separated from her normal companions; when she is out in the rain and cannot get to shelter. On any other occasion, continuous bleating can be taken to be a sign of distress. Call the vet.

Bloat: The rumen of the goat becomes blown up with gases which are unable to escape. Too much lush spring grass can cause it, or an excess of a particular food which disturbs the balance of the rumen's workings. The goat's left side bulges out and she may bleat or pant in distress. A drench of cooking oil will help to get things moving, and massage may help, but these courses of action are where the condition is not too far advanced. If she is like a balloon and in an obviously life-threatening situation, the vet should be called immediately. Always ensure that goats have hay to eat before they go out to spring pasture, and restrict the time spent there in the first weeks.

Brucellosis: A rigorous control programme in relation to cattle has now eliminated the disease in Britain. The disease can cause undulant fever in humans if infected, unpasteurised milk is drunk.

Caprine Arthritis Encephalitis (CAE): Goats can be positive carriers of the slow-acting virus, but the full disease may not necessarily develop. Its presence can be detected by the presence of antibodies in the blood. There is really only one long-term approach and that is to have all goats blood-tested. Anyone considering buying goats should ensure that they come from a CAE-free herd. Do not allow other people's goats to come on to your site unless they are known to be blood-tested and clear. Similarly, goats taken for mating should be clear. Most stud-owners insist on a current blood-test certificate before they will accept a goat for service. Owners of females should insist on similar confirmation with regard to the male.

Caesarian birth: In a difficult kidding and inability of the kids to be born normally, the vet will probably decide on opening the abdomen wall to save them. A goat straining without success for more than half an hour needs the vet.

Caseous Lymphadenitis (CL): Bacterial infection of the lymph glands which then exude pus. Consult the vet. Avoid buying goats from units that are not known to be disease-free.

Circling disease (Listeriosis): The microorganism Listeria monocytogenes affects the brain, making the goat lose coordination. Other symptoms are high temperature and pressing the head against the walls of the pen. The organism is soil-borne and can be found in poorly-made silage. Discard milk and call vet.

Cloudburst (False pregnancy): The goat is mated and shows all the symptoms of being pregnant, but what emerges from the womb is a burst of liquid. It is more common in older goats or those left unmated until their second year. Apart from the inconvenience of missing for that year, the cloudburst female usually comes to no harm and kids normally the following year.

Coccidiosis: This is caused by single-celled parasites called coccidia which are found in warm, damp areas such as bedding. A certain tolerance is shown as long as the burden does not become too great. Coccidia are passed out in the droppings and are subsequently ingested, causing reinfestation. Kids are particularly at risk, showing symptoms of diarrhoea, sometimes with blood in the droppings, and general straining and stress. Kids should always be reared on clean bedding. Avoid over-crowding and use a disinfectant that kills coccidial oocysts. If the condition causes concern, call the vet. The usual treatment is a drench for individual cases and general dosing in the drinking water for the rest. With proper management this condition should not appear. Coccidiosis affecting poultry does not affect goats, but that found in sheep does. Keep goats and sheep separate.

Colic: Overfeeding concentrates, suddenly changing the diet, or giving too much of any one foodstuff can all cause digestive upsets. This is not serious in the way that bloat is, but can be painful and distressing, with much bleating. The best thing is to walk her up and down. If this does not work, call the vet.

Collapse: This is a general name to describe the goat which collapses and is unable to move. It is important not to leave her on her side in case her breathing becomes restricted. Prop her on her front with a straw bale on each side and put a blanket over her. Call the vet immediately. It could be any number of things but expert help is needed without delay.

Cough: Goats do cough, and sometimes they sound just like humans when they do it. Most of the time a cough is nothing to worry about, but check that the concentrate feed is a nice coarse ration without too much powder in it. Fine dust in a feed can cause a cough, as well as a sneezing bout. More serious is the persistent cough, particularly if there is a high temperature. In these cases, consult a vet.

Cystitis: A kidney infection affecting females after kidding. If she is very vocal and strains to produce urine which includes blood flecks, contact the vet.

Diarrhoea: There are a number of conditions which can cause scouring (diarrhoea), from a simple digestive upset to a more serious bacterial infection. As an immediate treatment restrict all foods except hay and give warm water with glucose in it. A kid could be given this in a feeding bottle. A kaolin preparation is useful to help stabilise the droppings. If the scouring does not clear up by the following day, or if the droppings become bloodstained, call the vet.

Enterotoxaemia: No goat should ever have to suffer this condition, which is the worst of the goat diseases, because to vaccinate against it is so simple and effective. It is one of a family of soil-living organisms which cause tetanus, pulpy kidney and other serious but avoidable conditions. Symptoms are a drunken appearance and ultimate collapse of the goat which has severe diarrhoea and pain. She will often lie on her side, paddling her legs pathetically.

Entropion: The eylid turns inwards. This condition needs veterinary treatment before damage is done to the eye.

Fleas: A proprietary treatment such as that used for dogs and cats is effective. The bedding should be changed frequently to avoid a build-up of them.

Fly strike: If areas of the body become soiled with droppings, or if there is an open wound, bluebottle flies may lay their eggs there. In a short time these will hatch into maggots. Short-haired goats are rarely in this condition but Angora and Cashmere goats are obviously more at risk because of their coats.

Any goat which is seen to be pawing the ground or rubbing against a fence in the summer months should be investigated for fly strike. If it is discovered, clip back the hair, clean out the maggots and pus with disinfectant and apply antiseptic spray or cream. If this does not clear the condition, call the vet.

Foot and mouth disease: This is a notifiable disease which can affect all cloven-hoofed animals. It is rigorously controlled in Britain. If it does appear, DEFRA's policy is to slaughter all affected livestock and quarantine the area. Symptoms are lameness and dribbling at the mouth, which often has blisters around it. If these combined symptoms appear, you should notify the vet.

Foot rot: This is more commonly seen in sheep, but can occur in goats if they are on marshy ground in summer, or spend much of their housed time on damp, dirty floor litter. The bacterium enters the softened area of the hoof and sets up a local infection. This has a vile smell and quickly leads to lameness. The goat should be transferred to a concrete surface and separated from the others. Trim back the hooves and scrape out the areas of infection, cleaning the feet with soapy water and disinfectant. Dry them then confine her to a concrete area until it heals up. If you suspect that the other goats may have been in contact with it, but there is no evidence, it is a good idea to take preventive action to stop the disease spreading. Get the goats to step into a container of disinfectant, then stop them going on to the area where they have been grazing for a time. The organism is a fairly short-lived one but can survive for up to three weeks on the pasture.

Goitre: The thyroid gland in the throat swells up because of iodine deficiency. As the thyroid gland has a major influence on the metabolic rate of the body, it is a potentially serious condition, but reversible. If goats are given a mineral and vitamin supplement in their concentrate ration, this condition, or indeed any other deficiency trouble, should not occur. Care should be taken not to feed too much kale or other members of the brassica family such as cabbage and turnips. They have the effect of 'locking up' the available iodine if eaten to excess. The vet should be called if the effect of a normal feed supplement does not produce a noticeable improvement. It may be necessary to give larger doses of iodine but as it is a toxic substance, it should be left to the vet to decide what a safe dosage would be.

Heat stress: Although goats can stand a lot of heat, they should never be left in hot sun without access to shade, shelter and water. It is such an obvious thing to write, and yet there are still people who do it, like those who go to agricultural shows leaving their dogs locked up in cars to bake. White-skinned goats such as Saanens can suffer from sunburn.

Husk: The symptoms are frequent coughing caused by parasitic lungworms which, in turn, produce a form of bronchitis. Consult the vet who will prescribe the appropriate wormer.

Hypocalcaemia (Milk fever): A sudden deficiency of calcium in the blood, where rapid milk production drains away the body's reserves, can cause collapse of the goat. It usually occurs in late pregnancy or immediately after kidding. Death follows collapse unless a calcium injection is given without delay. Call the vet immediately. He will normally give an injection of calcium borogluconate. Recovery is usually magical: the goat gets to her feet as if nothing had happened. Avoid feeding too high a level of concentrates immediately before and after kidding. Do not milk her out completely for the first week, to avoid putting too much strain on her. Feed good quality hay at all times.

Hypomagnesaemia (Grass staggers): Staggers is a descriptive name for this condition because it can arise when animals go out on to new spring grass, and the main symptoms are lack of coordination and staggering. It is caused by a deficiency of magnesium when the flow of milk production depletes the body reserves. The vet should be called immediately to give a magnesium injection. If left untreated, the condition quickly becomes fatal. Milking goats lose a considerable amount of minerals in their milk output which is far greater than that of cows in relation to their size. A mineral and vitamin supplement as part of the concentrate ration will ensure that such deficiencies do not occur. Goats should also be given hay before they go out on new pasture in spring, and their time spent there should be restricted.

Johne's disease: This is caused by the bacterium Mycobacterium paratuberculosis johnei, and is a condition affecting cattle, sheep and goats. Infected animals suffer from a tuberculosis condition of the gut which ceases to be able to absorb nutrients. As a result, weight is lost rapidly and the animal weakens and dies. There is no treatment and the condition is invariably fatal. Infected animals need to be slaughtered and the offspring of infected animals tested.

Although rare, this disease should be taken seriously by all goatkeepers. Those buying goats should get assurance from the vendor that there have been no cases of the disease on the site. Diagnosis can be made from a laboratory examination of droppings.

Lameness: Observe goats carefully. If one holds up a leg or grazes on her knees, check her feet carefully, clean them and look for foreign bodies between the claws. (Bear in mind that goats do sometimes eat on their knees while browsing. It is when this is habitual that there may be a problem). If there is nothing obvious, see if one foot is warmer than the others, or she flinches when you touch one part. If the feet seem to be fine, check the leg joints for swelling. Contact the vet if in doubt.

Laminitis: This is lameness brought about by an inflammation of the hoof tissues. It is usually the result of an imbalance in feeding rations, as for example when too much spring grass is eaten. Too much concentrate in relation to hay can also contribute to it. Consult the vet who will prescribe treatment to reduce inflammation.

Lice: Any goat can pick up lice and it is important to keep a watch out for them. They are small and greyish and are found at the base of the hairs. A proprietary product or pour-on is effective. Change the bedding frequently.

Louping Ill: A virus infection causing encephalitis (inflammation of the brain). It is transmitted by ticks. Early signs are twitching and head shaking, followed by jerky movements. Call the vet.

Liver fluke: Found in wet areas, its secondary host is the snail. (See Worming).

Maiden milker: It can sometimes happen to males too. The milk should be drawn off, leaving a little behind each time, until it ceases of its own accord.

Mange (Mites): There are many different mites, some on the surface of the skin, some burrowing into the skin and some getting into the ears. They can all be treated with a veterinary insecticide, but the burrowing one is not as easy to detect. If there is an obvious skin condition which is causing discomfort, consult the vet. Ear mites should be suspected when a goat shakes her head often. A veterinary preparation can be sprayed into the ears to kill them. It is better to do it twice, with a couple of days in between applications. This will ensure that any eggs which subsequently hatch are also killed.

Mastitis: It is important to check the milk for the presence of clots which could indicate mastitis. (See pages 80-84). The condition is an infection and inflammation of the udder, and varies from very mild cases to massive and chronic infection. A mild case will often cure itself if the udder is given a chance to do so. An immunity may develop, as long as the udder is massaged to increase the blood flow. Homoeopathic remedies are also available. Where heavy mastitis infection is evident, there may be no alternative but to use an antibiotic administered by an intermammary syringe. Once the infection has cleared, a minimum of three full days must elapse after the last treatment before the milk is safe for consumption. Before that, there will be antibiotic residues in the milk.

Metritis: This is an infection of the womb which can be caused by introducing the hand into the womb to help during kidding, or where all or part of the placenta has been retained. It is recognised by a brownish, nasty smelling discharge from the vulva. (A lightish coloured discharge is normal after kidding.) The goat is off her food and there may be a higher than normal temperature. The vet should be called and he will normally prescribe antibiotic treatment.

Navel ill (Joint ill): Found in kids, the cause of this bacterial infection is almost invariably a dirty environment. Infection enters the severed umbilical cord, producing a red swelling around the navel. The infection can travel to the limbs, producing swollen joints. The vet will prescribe a course of antibiotic treatment, but once the infection has affected the joints, recovery is unlikely. Kidding pens should be thoroughly cleaned and disinfected before use, and clean fresh straw used as bedding. At the birth of the kids each one should have the severed umbilical cord dipped in tincture of iodine.

Orf (Contagious pustular dermatitis): This is a highly contagious virus infection affecting goats and sheep, and which can be caught by humans. Nasty blisters form around the corner of the mouth and nose. Isolate the goat and call the vet immediately. Wear gloves when handling the animal and do not let children go anywhere near.

Pine (Fading disease): Pine is an apt name for this rare condition. The animal appears to pine away for no reason. But there is a substantial reason. It is caused by a deficiency of the trace element cobalt in the diet. It is this element which enables the body to produce vitamin B12. It is more common in those areas where there are low levels of cobalt in the soil, and this is reflected in the quality of pasture. The immediate treatment is for the vet to prescribe cobalt sulphate, but a more long-term solution is to give a cobalt 'bullet'. This is swallowed and gives off cobalt slowly over a period of months. A good mineral and trace element supplement will ensure that enough cobalt and other minerals and trace elements are present in the diet.

Pink eye (Contagious kerato-conjunctivitis) (New Forest eye): This is a contagious eye infection which affects the eye membranes, making the eye red and sore. The eye weeps and there may be pus. Consult the vet who may recommend antibiotic treatment. Keep the goat isolated and wash your hands well.

Pink milk: A new milker or a heavy yielder will occasionally produce milk which is slightly pink. If you put it in a bottle and look at the bottom you will see the blood collecting there in a layer. It is the result of a few blood capillaries breaking in the udder and is normally nothing to worry about. The condition usually clears up of its own accord within a couple of days. If not, consult the vet in case it is mastitis.

Pneumonia: There are several forms of pneumonia and any persistent cough should be investigated by the vet. It may be causd by lungworm (see Husk) or it could be a bacterial infection which can produce a high temperature and serious lung damage. Veterinary treatment is essential, and careful nursing is important. Goats are not good patients. In fact, the relationship between the goat and her owner is important, and can often make the difference between recovery and decline. Give her a blanket to keep her warm and talk to her frequently. If there is a good relationship, she will respond, and this in itself can help her recovery.

Poisoning: Goats have a tendency to nibble and should be kept away from areas where known poisons are present. Examples are paintwork with lead-based paints, timber newly treated with wood preservative and areas where there is machine oil or diesel oil. The chances of such poisonings are rare: more common are cases of poisoning by toxic plants (See page 55).

Premature birth: A kid has a chance if it can be made to breathe, is kept warm and takes in colostrum. Clear the nostrils of mucus and rub all over with a towel until it breathes. If rejected by the mother keep in a box by the fire or under a heat lamp. Feed warmed colostrum and glucose with a small dropper every hour. Once able to suck of their own accord, they will probably survive.

Prolapse: This may be one of two types; the emergence of the cervix and vagina, seen as a mass of red tissue at the vulva, or the complete emergence of the uterus after kidding. Both conditions require the urgent attention of the vet who will replace them, using sutures and antibiotic treatment.

Pygmy goat syndrome: Confined to Pygmy goats, this consists of lesions usually appearing in the first year. There is no specific treatment, although bathing may help.

A continuously bleating goat, or one that is adopting an unusual posture should be investigated. *(Katie Thear)*

Ringworm (Dermatomycoses): A fungus infection, it is seen as a circular red patch with flaking skin and hair loss. It can be transmitted to other goats and to humans and should be treated with care. The vet will provide a fungicide.

Scrapie: One of a group which includes BSE in cattle and the human vCJD. It is a notifiable disease caused by infectious agents called prions.

Symptoms of Scrapie include muscle tremors, reduced appetite and reduced milk yield. There is no treatment.

Scurf: This is a general name to describe loose, flaking skin frequently seen in goats which have been winter-housed. It normally improves once they are out in the sunshine. It helps to bathe them and give a good brush to remove flaked areas. Ensure that they have a mineral, trace element and vitamin supplement.

Stones (Urinary calculi): Male goats are prone to this condition where the urine flow is restricted by a blockage. Veterinary advice should be sought, for it can cause extreme pain. Hard water areas can contribute to the problem, and the use of rain water or a fitted water softener should be considered. It is important that males are not fed too much concentrate in relation to roughage. Soaked sugar beet should only be given in small quantities. Some goatkeepers omit it entirely. Ensure that he drinks enough clean water.

Swayback (Enzootic ataxia): Rare in goats, this is usually associated with sheep. It occurs in kids whose dams have had insufficient copper in the diet. The result is poor neural development. When the kid tries to get up it sways from side to side at the back. There is no treatment and kids are best put down. Giving the mother a mineral and trace element supplement will give protection against the condition.

Tetanus (Lockjaw): A soil-borne organism which causes paralysis. There is no excuse for any goat having this condition. It is one of the organisms which the broad spectrum anticlostridial vaccinations will ward off. Every goat should be vaccinated once a year: consult your vet. It is also worth making the point that anyone working with livestock should have protection against tetanus. An injection once every five years will give protection: ask your doctor!

Ticks: These are nasty little parasites which are picked up in the summer from long grasses. They bite through the skin and then suck blood until they balloon out as a result. If you see one, do not pull it off, otherwise the mouth parts are left behind to cause an infection. Spray some flea spray on it and leave it. It will die and drop off. They are a nuisance more than anything, apart from their ability to transmit more serious conditions. (See Louping Ill)

Warts: These are occasionally found on the skin. They are benign tumours and generally disappear after a few months as immunity develops. A traditional remedy was to put the juice of dandelion stems on them. If they are frequent and bothersome, it is worth consulting a homoeopathic vet for advice.

Wounds: Any cut or graze should be treated with antiseptic such as an iodine or other veterinary spray.

Large wounds which are gaping or pumping blood should have urgent veterinary attention. Place a pad of cotton wool with bandage around it to make a compress on the wound. This will help to staunch the flow of blood until the vet arrives.

Wrynose: This is a hereditary defect which sometimes shows up in Anglo-Nubians. There is nothing which can be done to correct the crooked nose and it is better not to breed from goats that show this trait.

Regulations

All goatkeepers

All goatkeepers, regardless of how many goats they have, must abide by the following regulations:

- **Registration:** Register with the local DEFRA Animal Health Divisional Office (AHDO) who will issue a County, Parish, Holding (CPH) Number. After the registration, the owner is issued with a Herd Registration Document (HRD) that allocates a unique herd number.

- **Identification:** All animals born after 31st December 2009 must ordinarily have 2 identifying ear tags, which show both the herd number and the individual goat number.

- **Movement Record Book:** This must be kept up to date with details of the holding, the herd number, the individual ear tag information of the animals, and any movements to or from the holding.

- **Movement Document:** This must accompany a goat in transit to another site or show, etc, with details also recorded in the Movement Record Book. Details must also be sent to the local AHDO within three days.

- **Medical Records:** A Record of Medicines must be kept, indicating treatments given, the dates when commenced and finished and the identifying numbers of the treated animals.

- **Dead Stock:** Any goat over 18 months that dies or is slaughtered (except for human consumption) must be reported to DEFRA.

- **Notifiable diseases:** The following conditions are required to be reported to the authorities - anthrax (rare in goats), brucellosis (unknown since 1956), rabies (currently not in UK), scrapie, and foot and mouth disease.

Goatkeepers producing milk or dairy products for sale

Those selling milk or dairy products should get hold of all the regulations and advisory publications. (Contact local DEFRA offices, Environmental Health Departments and the Dairying Inspectorate). Relevant factors are:

- Milk is recognised in law as coming from cows, goats, sheep and buffaloes.

- Premises producing milk for human consumption must be registered (England and Wales) or licensed (Scotland and Northern Ireland) as a 'production holding'.

- Where milk is processed in any way, the premises must be registered or licensed as a 'dairy establishment'.

- Legislation covers all aspects of milk production, handling and processing, animal health, water supply, raw milk standards, premises and equipment, packaging and labelling, cleaning schedules, whey disposal and keeping records.

- All dairying estab¬lishments must produce a risk analysis programme that is agreed with their local Environmental Health Department. Once accepted, the producer is allocated a unique number and health mark which is then included on any packaging for traceability pur¬poses within the EU.

The following pieces of legislation are relevant:
Dairy Products (Hygiene) Regulations 1995.
Dairy Products (Hygiene) (Amendment) Regulations 1996.
Food Premises (Registration) Regulations 1991.
The Food Safety Act 1990.
Food Safety (General Food Hygiene) Regulations 1995.
Sheep and Goats (Records, Identification and Movement) (England) Order 2009
The Food Safety (Temperature Control) Regulations 1995.
The Cheese Regulations (Food and Drugs Act).
Weights and Measures Act.

Food Labelling Regulations 1996.
The Ice Cream (Heat Treatment) Regulations.

The following free publications are available from DEFRA Publications or from the Welsh, Scottish or Northern Ireland Agriculture Departments.

Dairy Products (Hygiene) Regulations 1995. Ref. No: PB2410
The Food Safety Act 1990 and You. PB2507
Guidance for Keepers in England Rules for identifying sheep and goats. PB13327
A Guide to Clean Milk Production. PB0341
A Guide to the Dairy Products (Hygiene) Regulations for Dairy Farmers. PB2338
Short Guide to the Dairy Products (Hygiene) Regulations for Dairy Farmers. PB2339.
A Short Guide to the Dairy Products (Hygiene) Regulations for Farmers Producing and Processing Milk from Goats and Sheep. PB2337

Goat manure

Finally, it is worth mentioning that used bedding straw and goat manure are best stacked in a compost heap that is then covered so that it can rot down over a period of time. As goat manure is relatively dry, the heap may need the occasional dowsing down with water. Adding a little lime in between the layers is a good idea to help 'sweeten' and maintain the pH value.

Once completely rotted, it can be used to good effect in the kitchen garden where it will add considerably to the fertility and structure of the soil. It is best to avoid spreading it on areas where goats are to be browsing, so that there is no possibility of transferring parasites. However, it must be said that once the stack is completely rotted and limed, the risk of parasite transference is minimal. The risk is when unrotted manure is applied.

The best time to incorporate it into the soil is during winter digging and bed preparation when earthworms will soon get to work so that their tunnelling activities incorporate air and improve overall drainage.

Commercial goatkeepers need to be aware that goat manure must not be allowed to percolate into and contaminate streams and water courses.

Reference section

Bibliography

Goats and Goatkeeping. Katie Thear. Merehurst Press.
Goat Husbandry. David Mackenzie. Faber & Faber.
All About Goats. Lois Hetherington. Farming Press.
Practical Goatkeeping. John & Jill Halliday. David & Charles.
The Goatkeeper's Veterinary Book. Peter Dunn. Farming Press.
Cheesemaking & Dairying. Katie Thear. Broad Leys Media Ltd.
The Goat Welfare Code. DEFRA.
Rules for Identifying Sheep and Goats. DEFRA.
Goat Health and Welfare. David Harwood. Crowood Press.
Goat Keeping. British Goat Society.
British Poisonous Plants. HMSO.
The New Goat Handbook. Ulrich Jaudas. Barron's Publishing. (USA).

Organisations

British Goat Society. www.allgoats.com
British Feral Goat Research Group. www.britishferalgoat.org.uk
Caprine Ovine Breeding Services. cobs.110mb.com
DEFRA Helpline. Tel: 08459 335577. www.defra.gov.uk
Goat Veterinary Society. www.goatvetsoc.co.uk
Harness Goat Society. www.harnessgoats.co.uk
Humane Slaughter Association. www.hsa.org.uk
Scottish Cashmere Producers' Association. www.cashmere-scotland.co.uk
Scottish Goatkeepers' Federation. www.scottishgoatkeepersfederation.com

Breed Societies

Anglo Nubian Breed Society. www.anglonubian.org.uk/
Bagot Goat Breed Society. www.bagotgoats.co.uk/
British Alpine Breed Society. www.britishalpines.co.uk/
British Angora Goat Society. www.angoragoats-mohair.org.uk/
British Boer Goat Society. www.britishboergoatsociety.co.uk/
British Saanen Breed Society. www.saanen.co.uk/
British Toggenburg Society. www.britishtoggenburgs.co.uk
English Goat Breeders' Association. www.egba.org.uk

Golden Guernsey Goat Society. www.goldenguernseygoat.org.uk
Old English Goat Society. www.oldenglishgoats.org.uk/
Pygmy Goat Club. www.pygmygoatclub.org
Toggenburg Breeders' Society. www.clinxx.co.uk/

Suppliers

Charnwood Milling Co. Ltd (feeds) Tel: 01728 622300 www.charnwoodmilling.co.uk
Cliverton Insurance Brokers (insurance cover). Tel: 01263 860388 www.cliverton.co.uk
D.C. Engineering (portable milking machines). Tel: 01983 533668
    www.dcengineering.co.uk
D.M. Harrison (homoeopathic livestock medicines). Tel: 01974 241376.
Electric Fencing Direct. Tel: 0870 609 2076 www.electricfencing.co.uk
Farmgate Feeds (feeds) Tel: 08457 228853. www.bocmpauls.co.uk
Frenchall Goats (goat equipment). Tel: 01638 750665. www.frenchall-goats.co.uk
Fullwood Ltd (commercial milking machines). Tel: 01691 627391.
    www.fullwood.com
Galen Homoeopathics (homoeopathic treatments). Tel: 01305 263996.
Gillrugs (goat rugs). Tel: 01297 33085. www.gillrugs.com
Goat Genetics (goat semen). Tel: 01785 824897. www.goatgenetics.com
Goat Nutrition (goat and dairying supplies). Tel: 01233 770780. www.gnltd.co.uk
Greenlands Insurance. Tel: 01970 615561. www.greenlands.co.uk
Ifor Williams Trailers. Tel: 01490 412626. www.iwt.co.uk
Ketchum Manufacturing (identification tags). Tel: 01737 812218. www.ketchums.co.uk
Rappa Fencing (electric fencing). Tel: 01264 810665. www.rappa.co.uk
Ritchey Tagg (identification tags). Tel: 01765 689541. www.ritcheytagg.com
Small Holder Feeds (feeds). Tel: 01362 822910. www.smallholderfeed.co.uk
Smith's Sectional Buildings (housing). Tel: 01630 673747.
    www.smithssectionalbuildings.co.uk
W. and H. Marriage & Sons (feeds). Tel: 01245 612000. www.marriagefeeds.co.uk

Index

Minerals 38, 47, 53
Movement Records 8, 10, 124

N

Notifiable diseases 124

P

Parasites 122, 123
Pasteurisation 84
Pasture 46
Penning 38
Poisonous plants 55, 121
Pregnancy 63
Pygmy and Pet goats 100

R

Rearing 76
Registration 9, 24, 76
Regulations 9, 124, 125
Rumen 18, 24
Ruminants 19

S

Shearing 97
Shelter 21, 46
Showing 106
Silage 53
Skin 93
Spinning 99
Storage
    feed 40
    hay 40
    milk 84

T

Teeth 15, 20
Temperament 21
Tethering 21
Training 45, 78, 102, 104

U

Udder 15, 18, 25, 81

V

Vaccination 78, 112
Vitamins 53

W

Water 56
Wild plants 55
Worming 111

Y

Yard 42
Yoghurt 86

Z

Zoonoses 110

Broad Leys
Self Sufficiency, Poultry, Smallholding, Livestock Books

Our other titles include the following:

Cheesemaking and Dairying Katie Thear. £7.95
Starting with Sheep Mary Castell. £7.95
Starting with Pigs Andy Case. £7.95
Starting with a Smallholding David Hills. £7.95
Starting with Bees Peter Gordon. £7.95
Starting with Chickens Katie Thear. £6.95
Starting with Bantams David Scrivener. £7.95
Starting with Ducks Katie Thear. £7.95
Starting with Geese Katie Thear £7.95
Starting with Turkeys Katie Thear £7.95
Keeping Quail Katie Thear £7.95
Incubation Katie Thear £6.95
DIY Poultry House and Run (A4 plans and cutting list) £3.00
Organic Poultry Katie Thear £12.95

Also available:

The Smallholder's Manual. Katie Thear. £25.00
Free-Range Poultry. Katie Thear. £19.99

Titles may be ordered from the publisher, prices correct at time of printing but subject to change without notice.

Our titles and more available from our online bookshop,
www.broadleys.org

Broad Leys Media Limited

Fron Dirion, Clogwyn Melyn, CAERNARFON, LL54 6PT
Tel: 01286 880847
E-mail: books@broadleys.org

The perfect companion to
Starting with Goats

K atie Thear was first taught how to make traditional cheese and dairy produce by her mother in their cottage in rural Wales.

In later life she taught Biology and Rural Studies and went on to acquire technical knowledge and experience of modern dairy practice at a commercial dairy

With her husband, David, she ran a smallholding where she regularly produced a wide range of dairy products.

Visits to dairies in Britain, France, Holland and the USA have added to her researches, making this one of the most comprehensive and practical books available on dairying.

Cheesemaking and Dairying
Katie Thear

Cheese, Yoghurt, Butter and Ice Cream

The ideal book for those with goats looking to utilise the milk and for those looking to start a small-scale commercial enterprise. Includes information on making cheese, yoghurt, butter and ice cream from goat's milk.

✓ How to make tasty cheeses
✓ Step-bystep instructions
✓ Soft and pressed cheeses
✓ Yoghurt
✓ Creams and Ice Creams

✓ Farmhouse butter
✓ Traditional recipes
✓ Equipment and supplies
✓ Where to begin
✓ Illustrated and up to date

Broad Leys Media Ltd

W ritten for those new to pigs, this book provides a good, sensible introduction to the subject. It looks at all aspects of practical management and handling, including housing, choosing breeds and stock, farrowing and health.

Concentrating on the older, more traditional breeds, it also covers free-range management, feeding, breeding and rearing, buying and selling.

Andy and Maureen Case are experienced pig farmers and smallholders. They have kept a wide range of traditional and rare breeds, and bring a wealth of 'pig-sence' to a subject that is all too often lost in technical detail.

✓ Pigs on a small scale
✓ Where to begin
✓ What you need to know
✓ Choosing a breed
✓ Buying stock
✓ Housing and handling
✓ Feeding and management
✓ Breeding and health

STARTING WITH
PIGS

Revised Edition

The Guide to Keeping Pigs for Smallholders and as Pets

Andy Case

A Broad Leys Publication

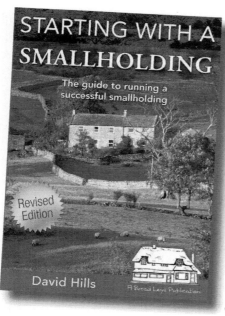

Written for those who are thinking of buying a smallholding and for new smallholders. This practical book provides essential guidelines to the care and welfare of livestock. It covers the efficient and enjoyable running of a small acreage

David Hills is an experienced smallholder himself and here he shares that experience for the benefit of those looking to change their life and take on a holding.

For those with a holding, he covers different enterprises that can be run for profit, discussing the resources required in terms of time and finance as well as the potential benefits.

For each project he gives guidance as to the amount of land, time, energy and money required to help you judge if the enterprise will be viable for you.

✓ What to look for in a smallholding
✓ Find the right place for you
✓ How to develop the skills needed
✓ Space, time, energy and costs
✓ Planning the priorities
✓ Garden and pasture care
✓ Animals and poultry